Jason Matias
#NakedThoughts

NakedThoughts

Written by Jason Matias

Published by Jason Matias

Copyright 2020 Jason Matias

Acknowledgments

To my mom. She didn't help me write this book. I feel like a lot of what I've put to paper lets her down. So, I'm writing this to mollify her. Thanks mom, I owe this brain to you.

To my dad who has insisted that I write a book for ages. I don't think this is what he had in mind, though.

To all the girls that I've loved before, I only want to love you more. - Tech9. But also, thanks. The damage you've wrought has inspired many of these pages.

To Angel, who's poked at me from day one about my writing and without whom this book would not exist.

To Lee, who suggested I "Put down my camera and write instead." I believe you meant that as an insult and, like a searing brand, your words of coarse affirmation have never left me.

To The Narrator (the semi-sapient alter-ego inside my head), I hate you. I love you. The way a pebble jams the wheel of a shopping cart, frustrating the pusher and creating a terrible chalky screeching noise, you make me pause and observe my observations. Thanks, I guess.

To my internet friends. Thank you for your support. We've never met. We may never meet. I like it that way.

Table of Contents

Foreword

By Angel Canann

When I say that this work is amazing, here's what I mean. I find a tremendous amount of honesty in it - sometimes more than I care to admit. It's easier to think lofty thoughts of ourselves and pretend that we don't judge, or look, or sometimes detest ourselves and everyone else in between the beautiful moments, but the insight in this work strips that pretense away.

In Jason baring his innermost thoughts to the world, he simultaneously removes the wall behind which we keep our own innermost thoughts and musings, and we are not able to deny them to ourselves in the face of his honesty.

I find myself reading through this thinking - oh yeah... I've thought that, and god I wish I'd thought that. I find myself being inspired and seeing the world in different ways that I never would have if I hadn't opened this up and walked through it.

It's the quintessence of humanity all together. The brightness and the darkness all wound up as one, right there before us, and there's not really any way to walk away from it, to stop being humbled by the truthfulness of it, or inspired by the possibility it offers without recompense. When I say it's amazing, that's what I mean, and that's why everyone should read it.

1

Preface

I'm writing this preface in a choir class. No, I don't sing. I haven't read a sheet of music in ten years or more. Now-a-days I'm a substitute teacher. Over the past few years I've been a dozen things: foreman in a popcorn factory, worker bee in a bindery, quality assurance lead in an aerospace manufacturing firm and an unemployed art salesman. All that after a career humping bombs in the Air Force. Now I'm becoming a writer. "Becoming" because, until I can get an idea to go from my head into someone else's without misinterpretation and confusion, I'll never be finished crafting this skill. Having been a teacher at both high school and college level, I know in my deepest depths and can attest, with evidence, that getting an idea into some people's skulls couldn't be done even if I wrote it on a bullet before sending it in.

This choir is currently murdering Hallelujah. Like, heel-stomping Hallelujah's face in the gravely mud, murder. It's June and even if the students aren't half as tired as the staff, they have still had enough time to learn how to make music together. Still, it's somehow pleasant to hear live music. When sound goes straight from vocal cord to eardrum, music really is alive. Even if it's a little bit ugly, it's a welcome companion.

You know, that's a lot like life and the experiences I'm sharing in Naked Thoughts. Life rarely shares her beautiful side, but she's always the best companion we've got.

I think that is what I do. I see the ugly side of life. Not the murder-stomping black side or even anything close to so deep a shadow. I record the ugly that doesn't get noticed. The face that disappears in a crowd. Obscure as such faces are, some of them have gems to share, and I pull them aside for an interview. Those encounters become Naked Thoughts.

Stockholm I NakedThoughts #1

I'm sitting at a bar in Stockholm, Sweden. I just paid 24 euros for a pulled pork burger, and it's worth every penny. Aside from the fact that I haven't eaten since before getting on an overnight train in Venice, this is the best burger I've had since before leaving Hawaii, 7 months ago.

There are seven men at the bar. Three of them are bald or balding. Those three are all under forty. My hair has been falling out when I run my hands through it. Too much stress. I'm worried.

Fully two thirds of the women who have walked by are wearing skin tight leggings. I judge each one. Fully two thirds of them don't belong in skin tight leggings.
I'm drinking a pint of Boston Lager at an increasing pace. I don't know what time it is, but my flight leaves at 5:30.

I feel that I should tip the bartender because she is pretty. It's not fair that men should be under such pressures. Her hair is tinted purple. It's nice… but she gets nothing.

Airport staff cruise around on scooters. The kind your eight-year-old niece rides up and down the drive way. These are more robust. They must support overweight personnel. I judge them too: performance and speed.

They all line up at the starting line in my head, next to the people pushing near-empty baggage carts. A curly haired white lady has the pole. She's determined.

I have six currencies on me. I'm international.

The old man next to me has retired from madly entering data on his iPad. He has a signature appeal. A classy air. An epic beard. He could be a mad scientist. Or the man pulling strings of operatives in the area. He could be watching a movie. Or surveillance footage. He might know that I'm writing about him.

It's quiet here.

Rooftop | NakedThoughts #2

I'm sitting on a rooftop in NYC. The view is Manhattan from Roosevelt Island. I just threw my kindle to the table in disgust. How some people publish books is beyond me. Is it true that you really cannot unlearn something? Shame. I'll have to wait for Alzheimer's.

The woman next to meet is reading "The Beach". I want to tell her to just watch the movie. The story is not compelling nor complex enough to warrant wasting memory on both the movie and the book. Especially if she keeps interrupting the book with her phone.

The setting sun casts beautiful light on her through the buildings on the other side of the horizon. Too bad I quit photography for today.

I had to stop to take a picture with my phone just now. The sun is down but these clouds will be on fire soon.

There is a group of guys on the adjacent building rooftop, staring at this building rooftop. Do they want to come here? Should I acknowledge them with a wave? Why are they not facing the sunset? This baffles me the same as when people leave the beach before sundown. Why did they even go to the beach? There are guys on the roof adjacent; I do nothing.

The faces of buildings are black to me now. The sides of structures to the left and to the right are orange, red, and warm.

The sounds of New York City are motors on the road, music over the water, applause rising from a dining terrace out of sight, and beer bottles up and down from the gentlemen to my left. I cannot hear the river and that makes me sad. I want a beer.

The woman just asked me what an "epitaph" is. I know it, but I look it up anyway.

The gents on the roof are gone. The light on the buildings is now yellow. The low hanging clouds have evaporated. I always miss that. In ten minutes I will remind her that the sun is setting. The colors will wow her, and I will take a picture with my phone. Because I quit photography for today.

The 1 Train | NakedThoughts #3

I'm sitting on the 1 train headed south from the upper west side. It's 2:26AM.

There is a multicultural couple sitting across from me. The young man is crying. His overweight, pasty-white girlfriend has not taken her eyes off of him. I cannot see her face behind her red curls. I admit, my curiosity is morbid.

Like a gentleman, I just dropped a cute young Canadian woman to her uptown apartment. I'm proud of myself for being on this train right now. Kinda.

There are purple cats fighting on the ceiling of an--- hold that thought, this is my stop. I still have another hour of train and a 20-block walk to get home. I need a bathroom.

A guy just cut me off on the stairs with his crew. His New York Yankee grey and white pinstriped cotton shorts are down around his thighs. I see ass cheeks through plain white boxer shorts right in front of my face. First thought; punch him behind the knee.

In the tunnel between 14th Street stations their voices echo. Their voices are hoarse like old people who have smoked too much or young people who have spent the last three hours yelling at horses. If I were ever to bet on horses I wouldn't yell or hoot or holler. When someone asked me if I picked a winner I would say, "Someone always does."

At the Queens-bound F train platform, I am the only person here. The sounds of NYC, a hundred feet below ground, are a chorus. The hum of fluorescent lighting. The clamor of flat steel against something hard echoes out from the tunnel. Screeching subway brakes and the muffled-but-loud sounds of trains passing through platforms above, below, and adjacent, but out of sight. The dirty, hot breeze mixing debris.
On the train. There are eleven people in this car with me. All tired. It's 2:55AM. There are ten now. All of them are in the rat race, I'm sure. The deodorant ad on the wall is hash-tagged #NYTOUGH. There are eleven tough rats on a track. Which one would I bet on? Would I bet on me? Would I shout, hoot, holler?

I wake up at Parsons, remembering I wanted to be home at midnight. I still have my phone, my wallet, my life: NY isn't so bad. It's 3:44AM, two stops and twenty blocks to a bathroom.

cellphone photo I took that night waiting for the train

Steak | NakedThoughts #4

I am sitting on the deck behind my parents' house, forced outside by sister and the obscenely high-pitched vacuum she hurls across the floor. The thing is older than I am.

I am so easily distracted by things that change, especially light. That's why I can't watch TV, and cannot concentrate at sunset.

Dinner has started. We're eating steak. I hate steak cooked by anyone but myself. Growing up, I felt like I ate cheap steak every other day. It was always tough and hurt my jaw to eat. No amount of A-1 sauce could fool my taste buds from its (lack of) flavor. I'm asked how I'd like it cooked. "However, the chef..." I don't even finish my sentence.

I'm supposed to be finishing an online job application for an e-commerce start-up, but I keep staring at the sun through the trees. I almost run and grab my camera, but let the impulse go. I do that more than you might expect; some photographer I am. The sun is below the horizon now. The golden sides of the leaves at the top of the trees is the type of gold that dilates pupils and makes people swoon. It's the color of greed, and the way the leaves sway gives the illusion of sparkle. If this type of gold could be harvested and sold, people would kill each other climbing to the tops of trees in the setting light.

Dinner was served. There was no A-1 steak sauce. I cut the smallest piece of steak though I am the largest person at the table. It did not go unnoticed. The sounds of dinner included the normal things you'd hear at the table. Silences filled by the sound of two pit bulls making out, or play-fighting. It's hard to tell the difference; it might be the same thing. I spend the time watching the juices of meat mix with the juices of zucchini and the creamy residue of mac and cheese. This is my custom at this table. I did learn that our two Rottweilers weigh 220lbs combined. I love big dogs.

Outside again. Twilight and crickets. When I kill a mosquito, I leave its remains as a warning to others. None heed. There are fireflies.

Virtual interviews are a farce. I wish I could stop and rerecord my responses in real life. The mosquitos are winning; I retreat. I'll spend all night applying to mildly interesting day labor, dreaming of nightly gold rushes.

Bryant Park | NakedThoughts #5

I'm lying on my back in Bryant Park. The grass feels wet though forecasted rain has yet to fall. The sky is getting dark. The city actually seems a little bit quieter. Less sirens. My guess is that people take a break from getting hurt, hurting each other, and stealing things around dinner time.

There are less people in the park than before. Their noise replaced by "Love's Labour's Lost" performed over speakers at one end of the park and the two women nearby made deaf by years of high decibel story telling between each other. It's nice to hear their accents though.

Yoga, like yawning, is spontaneous in the park. Little kids pretend to do yoga like adults next to adults pretending to do yoga like Instagram. There are a few upside-down yogis opposite the play. They shake beneath each other's weight. Other people try not to look.

When people talk about others we call them gossipers. When people talk about themselves we call them self-centered. What else is there to talk about, I wonder. I'm hearing a lot about some woman from the two on my left. They are gossiping. I'm telling you about it; I am gossiping.

The sky is a mixture of black and the blue of a glow-in-the-dark stick if it were almost out of energy. A little girl's rubber-band-launched paper helicopter stands out against the subtle light. Her father misses every attempt at catching it.

80% of people are wearing head phones and/or staring at their phones, like me. All of us secretly hoping to meet someone new. Someone attractive. Someone who simultaneously makes us feel good about ourselves and makes us feel as though we could be better. If it doesn't happen in the moments between looking at our phones and looking at our phones...

I'm no exception. I'm stealing glances all day long. No dinner breaks for me. I look up hoping for eye contact, but prospects keep disappearing as I write. If the sky gets any darker we all will be floating blips of illumination in crossing isolation. I want someone to notice me. That's why I write these vignettes; I'm self-centered. I'm just waiting for the rain to force me to go home.

Skunks | NakedThoughts #6

I'm reclining in a lawn chair. It's close to 11:30pm and I am at a cabin near Schroon Lake, in upstate New York. This is the real NY. The rolling hills and great lakes, New York. The old growth forests and Niagara Falls, New York. This is the kind of NY where you place rocks in a circle to burn tall piles of birch and oak while sitting in a bigger circle drinking a beer, New York. That's what I've been doing for four nights. Or, at least it's been my favorite part of the last four nights.

I spent the last three days photographing a wedding. The bride is a beautiful woman. A blond fitness competitor. Her husband, a beautiful man; I'm not afraid to say it, is a fitness competitor and soldier. They invited me to their cabin; I built epic fires. Last night's fire lit tonight's fire. Figure that one out.

My feet are up on the fire pit. My toes are learning how to cope with the invisible reach of the heat. My socks are dryer than they have ever been.

The air tonight is so cool. The breeze blows the fire off my toes and pulls in the scent of pine from the forest. The sounds of New York are the crackling of the fire and the occasional shift of its weight. The crickets compete for love above the bristling of leaves moved by the breeze. There are birds' occasional conversations on the wind. And behind me a skunk is tearing apart a garbage bag.

Wait, what?

In the inky dark beyond the firelight, a white stripe slinks across the covered patio in search of a few drops of Corona mixed with Whiskey, Bud Light, and cigarette tea leaking from the corner teat of an industrial garbage bag.

By the light of my flashlight, our gazes meet. Awkwardly stunned, we both realize that we did not have a plan for this event. I yell at him like he's my dog. "Hey! Geet!" He ignores me as though he were trained in a different language. I reach for a rock and burn my hand on it. Damn I build a good fire. My cursing and thrashing send the skunk darting to the corner of the porch. I find him with my light and, sure enough, I'm staring down the ass end of a rear firing cannon. There are 20 feet between us. I find myself wondering if its spray will light on fire like a fart does on Youtube.

I decide this would be better discovered on Youtube.

I'm inside the cabin now. Writing. A well-aimed rock (at the side of the cabin) granted me the knowledge of Mr. Le Pew's den; right beneath the porch. I almost didn't go back out to dowse the fire pit. I'm not afraid of nature. I'm afraid of bathing in tomato sauce.

I'm sitting on the top of a mountain in NY. No, this isn't a hiking photo adventure. This rounded top is owned by some self-made man and I am cutting his grass. Not at the moment though; it's lunch time and I'm doing jaw exercises so that I can fit this monster club sandwich into my mouth (I don't remember joining any club). There are some vegans out there trying to change my ways. I like your food, ambassadors, but I prefer to eat things that had parents.

You can see across the Hudson River from here. West Point is on the far bank trying to make men out of college students. Across from me is my step-father, sitting on a bucket. The wind is blowing, and it's a bit cold when the sun disappears. So, I had to convince him to sit out in the open. "It's getting nipp'ly out here real quick." he says.
"I know," I reply, "That's why I'm out here; one of these days is going to be the last nice day of autumn. Then what?"

The sounds of autumn are the ceaseless wind and the dry falling leaves. The occasional rolling hum of a passing train floats up from the river bank. There are hawks circling. They don't make noise, but I imagine a 'whooshing' sound, like a flapping cape.

The trees are attacking. Acorns are falling from branches like blind kamikaze pilots out to get me. There are dozens of misses around me in the grass; I'm anxious. Actually, when the wind blows hard and the tree limbs swing, it looks as though the trees are hurling acorns at me. Tree Ents with projectiles.

Good thing trees aren't our natural enemies. There are coyotes in these hills, though. Coyotes also prefer to eat things that had parents. Things that make you go "awe", like cute bunnies and people's dogs. That's not cool. That's not as acceptable as a bologna sandwich. Baby pigs are cute though...

Plus one for the vegan ambassadors.

Flaircopters | NakedThoughts #8

I'm eating McDonalds on the steps of the NY Public Library. I'm a little upset that I wasn't asked to be super-sized. Before you say, "Gross!" Know that I ate vegan last week. My body can't handle that much good karma. I'm balancing.

The ambiance is set by the flashing of cameras. I'm sitting next to the famous granite lions that somehow represent learning and wisdom. I feel famous.

Further mood lighting provided by the NYPD, complements of the sour looking chap in an ugly green Acura. The cops are staring at my food. Rude.

Earlier today my mother offered me McDonalds. That was eight hours and a hundred miles ago. I should have gone. She only wanted company.

I defend my territory against a roach.

I'm in a quitting mood today. I don't have much to quit from. I should quit quitting. But the act of quitting quitting would be doing the very thing I was trying not to be doing.

I dunk my cheeseburger into sweet and sour sauce.

In front of me, two guys walking together drag their feet as they slink along. They're taking too long to move on. I inwardly hope the guy launching the LED helicopters into the air with a rubber band launches one directly into their faces and they tumble into traffic.

The other sounds of New York are the faux camera shutter sounds of phone cameras. Japanese women throwing audible peace signs. The endless repeating of thousands of explosions housed in steel blocks propelling people downtown.

Now I'm playing with the "Flaircopter" and trying to take pictures. My phone joins the chorus of sounds. A crowd gathers. Tony, the hustler, makes as much as $500 a night selling these things. He gives me one for free. A middle-aged lady with curly hair and glasses and a cigarette in her mouth just bought the cheap toy from him. She launches it into the air while exhaling cyanide through a smile. Our inner children are balancing our karma.

I'm bouncing in chest deep water so almost-perfect it makes you say "damn", and snap your fingers the way only "almost perfect" can. It's the perfect temperature, but the water is dark from the black sands. There are light waves, but the ground is rocky and pinches your feet. I'm surrounded by happy Filipino children, but there is a big white American in front of me who won't stop talking about something. Almost perfect.

Business. Me. My house. Me. Wave wall. Me. Business... The other sounds of the Philippines are children; loud in foreign tongues. My father is in conversation with Jonel, who's portrait I just took; a village elder, dying salt farms, techniques, murmurs. A stone skips once and ends in a splash. Kids cheer anyway. All against the backdrop of the wind and the waves and the babbling of this dude: Oil. Me. Development. Me. Business. My house. My wall...

I don't hear too much of what he is saying. He's a nice guy, but my attention is on the sky. The east horizon is reaching toward the west like the spreading wings of a hawk, and it's gathering color in its feathers as if it needs the light for flight. Inside, I struggle with "to shoot, or not to shoot". I'm having another I-quit-photography-for-the-day. Artists know: the struggle is real.

The colors are compelling, though. Later, I will desaturate the pinks so the world will believe the Philippines' unbelievable skies. I scramble over the rocky shallows mumbling something about going to take a picture, fearing I missed the best of it already. Then tip-toe back into the ocean as if the rocks are egg shells to balance upon with my camera and my salty tripod. Precarious. The show is almost over.

The wing is on fire. The hawk has become a Phoenix. Beneath it I am waving down pump-boats to become part of my composition. At what felt like the last minute I realized that I had my own pump boat and driver. Finger snap, duh!
How did I miss that? This boat brought me here. We get him to swing the boat around and bam! We have photography.

Photo of Jonel

I'm sitting at Alex Grey's party. Current emotion: jealousy. In front of me is the most epic bonfire I have ever seen. A seven-foot tree trunk burns on its end like a smoke stack. Fire and sparks shoot 40' into the air to become the starry night sky. Why haven't I thought of this?! The fire is manned by Wolverine; I'm jealous of his sideburns.

Illuminated bat wings float by.

Walking through Alex Grey's home is like being poked with an electric cow prod in the eyes. Stimulating. Talk about humble beginnings; this artist started out drawing anatomical pieces for medical journals. But heck, even the greatest temples are only built with stones.

A genie-fairy-elf-unicorn asks me who I am supposed to be. "Not me." I tell her. She continues to be confused. This is a pre-Halloween party. Halloween: a time when personalities pretend to be themselves differently. I want to go to a Halloween party filled with actors. It'd be full of ghouls and monks and sexy dominatrix instead of people only dressed like them. Lucifer would be damning people, and no one would take that witch's apple. I would be a Bulgarian castle builder bent on selling someone a castle. I'd have pictures of the scariest, most brooding place in the darkest forest and try to book showings.

I don't have Halloween spirit, actually. I bought a masquerade mask for $2.19 at the Dollar General on the way here so that I could wear it on my head, because I didn't bother to do my hair today. I can't even pretend to be me lately.

A yeti wearing a sombrero just gave me the nod. Hola.

Alison Grey is telling me about her temple. "Whenever you love, you build a temple." she explains. "Then I have broken ground many times." I think to myself. The Greys are building an actual temple. The economics of love are contributions. Contributions make spirituality into religion. She tells me she loves me and gives me nine inches of hemp. Now I have to dig a new hole.

I have nine inches of hemp and knots to tie. One for each obstacle that keeps me from achieving my dreams. I have ten knots so far. Nine are for invariably being afraid of something. The tenth for being so easily distracted.

The sounds of tonight are: dub step. At least, I think that's what it's called. The undertones of conversation from brand new art experts float on the air. Behind me they discuss political pop music. I will never un-hear this conversation. The Temple of Grey is nonjudgmental, I tell myself. In my ear, my inner costumed ego nags me about bringing girls to my castle. "I'm pretending not to be you right now." I tell him, errr- myself. Besides, I have these knots to tie.

Hippies are dressed like hippies, dancing like hippies, in a circle. They must have forgotten their costumes, too.

A skeleton with an LED top hat is Instagramming next to me. Now I am Instagramming. It's contagious. I wonder if I'm in his picture.

A neon hoop spins around an invisible hooper in the dark and Satan dances to the pace of the fire. This is as close as I've been to a rave.

The exercise with the hemp has shown me that there is really only one knot that needed to be tied on this rope. There's not enough rope left to tie it. Irony. When I finish I am to throw my knots into the epic fire, if Wolverine will let me. I throw my mask in, too. I don't need a costume to fake it. I wonder if I'll need one to make it.

Speed Reading | NakedThoughts #11

I'm in NYC. My plan is to walk 'that way' until I find pizza. I realized on the train that life is nothing like I thought it would be. I'm reading "A Tale for the Time Being", which is a story about Nao and Ruth who are simultaneously at odds with their immediate future, though one is alive and the other presumably dead.

I've been walking through life much the same way I walk in the city: turning blind corners.

Yes, at the moment I'm one of those people with my nose in the phone and in others' way. I may have just passed the woman of my dreams but missed it. I'm in no condition for love anyway; all I've got is blind corners and bad decisions ahead.

I, not so overtly, look down and read people's texts when they pass me. It's an exercise in speed reading.

If I could have any talent in the world it would be to read really, really fast. Every time I learn something I wish I already knew it. There is so much to learn, and my attention is so short: I have to read fast. I've been trying to use this new thought to motivate myself to learn Japanese. I also want to learn how to paint in Photoshop and play the violin.

I want to learn to speak languages to make the world smaller, to learn to paint because I pretend to create images for a living; and to learn to play the violin because I want Logan, my son, to learn to play the strings. His mom says it's a girl's instrument, though. I met a guy in Marrakech who spoke 13 languages and, you know what? I bought a ton of shit from him. I'd also enjoy reading foreign people's texts when they pass. New York is full of people who pass words around with differently weird, squiggly lines.

Learning is meaningless if you do not do anything or go anywhere. There is no greater waste of your time than to be inspired and do nothing. I'm at the corner of Nothing Doing and Nowhere Going. Pizza is around one of these bends.

The girl next to me is writing in symbols. Might as well be hieroglyphics. But she's discussing weed with her friend so maybe that's what 建議必 means. Now makeup, she's not wearing any. Now Chinese. She caught me trying to draw characters in my notes app. Now she's gone.

Imagine letters weren't squiggly but wriggly? When you received a message it would be one image that wriggled into new images at exactly the speed you could comprehend them. Then you never see it again. Kinda like a Snapchat meets Mission Impossible. You would *really* have to pay attention.

I may have just passed another potential girl of my dreams. Maybe one day she'll read this NakedThought while causally speed reading on someone's else's phone and find me and by then I'll have straightened out these corners and everything will turn out all right.

I found pizza.

I'm sitting on the front porch rubbing my left foot. I think that instead of going back to writing cover letters that typically end in me lying about my enthusiasm for X's and Y's opportunities, I'd like to tell you about a puppy. Roxy is a Rottweiler that, at one point in time, fit in the palm of a hand and made whisper-like whimpering noises that could melt the heart of a starving brown bear after a winter's worth of nightmares. Her cold little nose could probably have stopped global warming.

By the time she fit into two hands, her mom (my mom), had taught her a neat little chase game where she scooted her foot around and little Roxy chased after it. Probably slipping and sliding on our creaky hardwood floors with ears flopping the way puppy's ears flop. I'm sure Roxy never took her eyes off mother's white shoe.

As I said, I'm sitting on the porch rubbing my foot after a half hour of playing with these Rotties. They no longer fit in any number of hands, btw, and my feet aren't quite fast enough to play this game they still love. The sounds of suburbia are the defining sound of emotional isolation. Also, a school bus deposited a child who just walked by while, somehow, not noticing 300 pounds of dog and a tiny human (me) silently counting his steps. Another (lesser) dog in another house somewhere beyond the hedge that keeps these homes safe and alone is now barking the youngster's perceived trespass. There is a nuclear-powered pit bull quietly panting and softly whining at me with a red rubber netted ball between her legs. Throw to me.

It seems to be that my mother, who is still "29," no longer plays that scooting foot game with Roxy, and Roxy never learned how to play nicely as a now, very big puppy. So, my foot hurts and I am no closer to getting this job that I don't want. Roxy watches my foot. The pit watches my hands. Maybe I'll just send this as my next cover letter.

Toys R Us | NakedThoughts #13

I am at Toys "R" Us. We're shopping for my son Logan, seven months old. I don't remember this place as a kid. The grandparents have a weird, determined, happy look on their faces. Paul still hasn't met Logan. Logan lives in Phoenix, I live in Hawaii (technically), and this is NY. The world is too big these days.

Grandma grabs a shopping cart. I say, I'm here to get one toy. She affects not to hear. The grandparents want to dote.

I must be a bad parent because I hate all this noise. As a kid I enjoyed the sound of Bruce Lee beating people up with nunchucks that whistled through the air, but the sounds of Toys R Us are the wails of a hundred different toys. Two moms bash dads at the end of the isle while someone's kid ponders Simon Says. I kinda wanna play Simon Says. It was three blues then red, green, red, yellow; damn-it. Five-year-old's these days. I refrain. I'll just buy the app.

I keep turning off all the toys as I walk by them. That's kind of fun. The more I touch stuff the more things begin to feel familiar. Transformer toys make me feel gooey in a place I haven't noticed in a while. I could feel my posture melt. Good thing no one saw. I can't have strangers thinking I'm a nice guy. "Shake it off." I tell myself as I turn Bumblebee off.

I walked between a toddler and the toy he was ogling and felt like I should apologize. "Sorry, bud."
"It's okay, man." He replies with a tired sigh. Mind blown.

I find a hammer with sound effects for Logan. Pictures of him hitting his mom make me smile. This kid needs to grow up so I can play with Transformers again.

I walk past a set of "cute and cuddly" dogs that bark when you walk by, twice. I experience a vision of punting Ron Burgundy's dog off a bridge. A little girl catches me turning all the dogs off.

Remember Legos? When he's older, I can feel like a giant when I crush his mini cities in the dark. Godzilla. We'll have to build a Japanese city and a US one. Complete with Battleships-style peg board in between. This way Godzilla can destroy half the world in only a few minutes. Little boys need destruction, I need to play with toys, and we all would like to pretend the world is a much smaller place.

I've decided I like being on planes. I have an affliction. It's called Wanderlust and I have a rare strain. Instead of an intense yearning for travel I have a pang for not wanting to be where I am. After all, traveling is not only about going places, it's about leaving them, too.

Getting to a plane is not nearly as enjoyable as being on one. My personal bubble is reduced to the volume of my lungs. I'm treating the airport like an amusement park; I'm standing in line for the TSA-experience. The Jewish "gents" behind me are laughing on my neck. Their breath stinks, it's cold, and their entire conversation belongs on a list of things people wearing yamakas shouldn't speak about in public... next to eavesdroppers.

The TSA woman looks uncomfortable as I stare straight through her eyes. I can't help it. She looks suspicious. Why can't I check her ID? With all this identity theft we hear about, one can't be too careful. She now knows my name, travel plans, and the address I lived in three moves ago because I haven't updated my license. I don't know anything about her besides that she doesn't like her job today. This is not quid pro quo. She squirms on her stool. I still got it.

I'm undressing on a table now. I know some guys who get paid big bucks for this. Next, my clothes get to go on a ride, they love this part.

"I've been telling you for 45 minutes that you DON'T NEED TO REMOVE YOUR IPAD." says Jamaican TSA lady.

"Excuse me." I repeat until she notices me. "I haven't been standing here for 45 minutes."

I want to tell the lady at the end of the ride that I like her hair, but she won't make eye contact with me, despite my obvious intent on speaking to her. I just want to brighten her morning. I wonder if my friends get it this bad the morning after.

I could enjoy stripping.

WENDY'S! My morning is saved.

FML. They're serving breakfast. Who the fuck goes to Wendy's for breakfast. Disappointment.

The sounds of Delta Terminal Charlie-70 are: not a friggin' peep. Everyone is looking at their phones in silence. Desperately trying to drown out the terrible New Age Jazz dripping from the speakers with the commotion of their busy digital lives. My stomach is growling audibly.

The digital realm is constantly, simultaneously, the Now-life and the forgotten past. Everyone is constantly searching the past to be present in other people's lives while desperately sharing their present only to watch it be consumed by the Internet and disappear. It's kinda like when we take a bite out of a good meal.

Once it's down the gullet it's gone. Unceremoniously removed from the conscience world. The Internet eats our lives like potato chips.

Damnit! Everyone has Wendy's.

A flight to Miami is boarding. All the cute girls are on it. The attendant separates the crowd with a red-ribboned stanchion. The plane will regurgitate them into Florida's economy. Planes are kinda like birds that way. Bird food lives twice, disappears twice. The world is wild and there's never enough to eat.

when I watch aircraft take off I alway imagine riding
on top of on a wing

Karma I NakedThoughts #15

Sunset is still the most magical moment of every day. According to Zen Master Dōgen, there are 6,400,099,980 moments in each day. That's 6.4B moments to be present, to be thankful, and to tend your karma. Though, karma for the sake of karma is not karmic.

The other day in NYC I was wandering about. Early for dinner and, of course, hungry, I strolled past a homeless couple with a 'my wife is pregnant' sign, also claiming to be hungry. I normally give my change out to people on the streets; it feels good and I hate carrying loose change, anyway. It makes my pants bulge in the wrong place. But, this day, I didn't have any change and felt bad, so I actively avoided eye contact the way a guilty dog does when he knows he's done bad by his human.

Having been pretty broke myself of late, I decided to buy some cheap pizza to keep my dinner date bill down. I'm still early so I bought three slices and walked them back to the couple.

You know how when you text a romantic interest and they don't respond? That sucks. I have a girl that I message who ritually ignores me for weeks at a time. I text her just for practice these days, it keeps my ego in check. Anyway, people just want to be acknowledged.

Turns out he is a homeless Vet; not the sharpest tool in the shed, but nice enough. Sitting on the sidewalk watching people walk past provides a different perspective of NYC. Considering people generally ignore each other anyway, it's not that much different from standing on the sidewalk in NYC and watching people walk past. Besides, we were pretty happy with three chicken parm pizza slices and military talk.

Anyway, I never said anything about this experience because talking about it seems counterproductive to tending one's karma. But sitting on this plane watching the sunset over the starboard wing while listening to the whiney hum of jet engines underpinning a conversation on what the federal government should spend money on brings it all to a point. I had two choices, write about this, or argue with them.

It is not the federal government's job to feed the homeless. It is your job, our job, to help the people around you. Man cannot stand on the shoulders of giants if all the would-be giants are on their knees. And, a nation is the collective actions of individuals. People help people. Nations help nations. Quit being selfish and looking for someone else to fix your problems: good neighborhoods are created by good neighbors. I wish I took up that argument.

We do it for our vanity. Karma = spiritualized vanity. Philanthropy = commercialized karma. When I'm rich I'll buy pizza for an entire avenue of people sitting on their asses watching other people go by. I'll film it and cite karma in the interview but label it philanthropy in the YouTube description. It'll be just another day in NY, and I'll be eating pizza to keep my dinner date with the tax lady cheap. Women love free dinners. Afterwards, she'll ignore texts for an entire year.

Can you believe that these words are reaching you right now? I mean, I'm writing in real time and you probably won't read this for a few weeks or even years, but I'm reaching you. And, I guess, you're reaching me, too. Who are you? Where are you? Are you really as awesome as I imagine you are? Since I question the idea, do I doubt your awesomeness? Does that make you dreadful company? Or me? Could you be as boring as I fear? I hope not. However, you know what they say, "Hope is the universal folly".

Actually, I made that up about three seconds before I wrote it.

Where was I? Oh, right: Where am I? That seems to be the question these days. I have a few rules that I tell people about. Rule number one: no complaining. I spent three years complaining, once. None-the-better for it. So, I gave-up. Rule number two: no quitting. Just kidding. Rule number two: don't ask questions you're not willing to answer. You know this online dating thing? Conversations are like cat and mouse. One doesn't run unless the other is chasing. I mean, my Tinder collection is international, but I tire of the back and forth. So, I answer a question before I ask it. Conversation is halting, but who looks at trading cards after they've assembled the deck?

Aw man, I'm lost again. It's midnight here. I'm in a dark room in Washington. Rain patters on the skylight. Pit-pit-pat-pit. Patter-patter-pit-pit-pat. I try to type to the pace, but the words don't come fast enough. I like the rain; the sound keeps me from thinking about you. The only other sounds of tonight are keys rapping on this computer and the heater that doesn't seem to stop. The temperature is 35 degrees outside. I keep telling myself it's not that cold. I once vectored a helicopter to our rescue site in the evergreen forests of North Pole, Alaska. With wind chill it was negative -85(ish) degrees. That was cold. Story time for another night.

Truth told, I'm a bit "into the drink". I'm writing in a bar and I don't remember the bar's name. Is that rude? A shot of whiskey, a white Russian, two rums mixed with two cokes. I forgot to eat. I'm still standing straighter than a garden wall, so to speak, but my mind is swimming. When I hit 'Send' I will communicate this loosely proofread nakedthought to you faster than I could communicate the color of red to the person sitting across from me. Faster than an arrow makes that ssshpt't sound. Faster than you sounded that ssshpt't sound in your head. That's dangerous. My facebook updates hit 7,000 people in 40+ countries in less time than it takes for hair to grow the length of two atoms. Faster than I could politely tell the woman next to me that her hair was in her drink. Actually, I thought that was funny and moved to watch from another table. You get my point.

But do you? Are you as pensive as I assume you are? Do you consider that when you answered the question this book just asked you, you were speaking to a person in the past? Is that time travel? Hell, I might not even be alive, like actors from old movies. Do answers to old questions make the past present? Some people prefer the drunk version of me. Do you need a drink now? Cheers.

Coffee | NakedThoughts #17

I'm sitting in Anthem. It's a coffee shop in Tacoma, Washington. I feel like I need to tell you that because everybody is always asking me where I am. I'm on the Internet. Do places even matter anymore?

I'm trying to visualize time as a piece of paper. I don't remember what I was watching on the coffee shop TV, but I remember hearing, "...as events unfolded..." It was probably the news trying to incite modern racism like it's retro and back in fashion. I'm so tired of hearing black and white in the same sentence. Have you noticed that in any other context the term African-American is used? Words are so powerful.

The sounds of today are: a cappuccino machine. The shrieking, slicing cacophony of caffeine made ingestible. Does it really have to be that loud? I can't even describe the sound of this thing other than, it sounds like a cappuccino machine. I don't even like coffee.

Thinking of coffee always reminds me of a story from Tech School. After falling asleep in class one day, my military training instructor forced me to drink a mini-keg of black coffee. He stared at me the entire time, too. His eyes danced with amusement. When I think of coffee and the imagined steam wafts in front of my face, I see his bald head and crooked smile as if it were a mirage. I wish these places called themselves something other than coffee shops. Then I wouldn't feel like a black sheep when I come to thieve their WiFi. Did you know coffee was invented in the Middle East? It was outlawed in Europe for decades because the pope deemed it offensive, having been created by heretics. But, he drank it in private. Irony. The world runs on caffeine today. An everyday example of the futility of bigotry.

The sound of women's voices drags me out of my reverie. Around me people meld into their digital lives. Women chat to each other and men steal glances. There is something powerfully beguiling about the excited eyes of a beautiful young woman. Let me be honest with you; I don't like coffee, and I have Internet at home. What I don't have is women to tease me, and the quiet commotion of civilization to distract me. You have to go outside for that, and take refuge in your private life in public.

So, this thought unfolds, and time unfolds. Why do people assume time is folded? If time is folded, how large is each side? Does the size of something infinite even matter? Do the sides collapse onto the plane of existence with a big puff of air like when you drop a big book? Does it make a noise?

No. People make noise with their opinions and interpretations. The news argues racism with prop coffee cups that steam for hours, and I write in black on white. Don't they know the world would mesh if only they let it alone?

Blind Date | NakedThoughts #18

I'm at Starbucks and I'm too exhausted to leave. I'm drinking tea, not coffee. I hate coffee, as you know. There's a blind date happening next to me. Old people. The future of a bachelor, and the fear of a woman who only meets bachelors. My future. Sad face.

He's balding. She looks like she crochets too much. So far they've talked about traffic and work messenger programs. Now, they're on their non-adulthood-ness. At this point the denial is shameful. He just finished talking about how he does not like coffee, beer, or liquor. She agreed enthusiastically. Thus, they don't feel like adults. Because: beer and coffee are adult things. Note: we are sitting in Starbucks.

Now they are discussing their favorite Mai-Tai's. She likes something with lemon in it. Do they remember how this conversation started?

I sneak sidelong looks for appraisal purposes. He looks like he bought his outfit today. I have something against people who wear hiking boots that have never been off the pavement. His Merrill's look like they're still on the display at REI. Maybe that's just style in Seattle.

Meanwhile, in other corners of the room, the barista is really hot. She meets glance for glance without shame.

Boss. She looks expensive. Now that I think on it. Women, in terms of relationships, represent nothing but an expense, and my books can't handle them. I'll still go for the number. It's practice for better days. I wonder if the guy next to me is wondering how much the night will cost.

I feel like every encounter with someone you don't know is a blind date of sorts. It's like you're a telemarketer walking down the street, and you accidentally walk into the person on the other end of the line, and have to make the sale in person. Awkward.

Ever buy a TV at Costco only to find out that the box is too big for your car? In Nebraska? This guy has. He's a "traveler." At least he didn't use the word "adventurer." I might have flipped out. Every web bio I read these days says that said person "loves adventure!" Shopping for a TV in Nebraska in a tiny car is asinine and so is his story.

If his tiny, overburdened car was rammed off the road by a frothy-faced brown bear and the TV got water damage from the icy stream he crashed in... If he had to build a sled out of some sapling trees he knocked down, sewing his drop-top with the seams of his shitty leather seats... If he then trudged through inclement weather throughout the night, by the light of the full moon, with a bear on his heels, back to Costco to get a replacement, and ended up landing a first date with the chic at the exchange counter... If that happened, then

51

buying a TV at Costco in Nebraska and shoving it into your tiny car would have been a story worth telling, and this blind date would be more interesting to listen to.

Emptiness | NakedThoughts #19

I'm at "work". Not my work, someone else's work. They just pay me to do it. It's dusty and dry. My nose has been bleeding from the dryness. I pick it because it irritates me. That, in turn, irritates my nose. Vicious cycle.

I can't tell if there is music playing or if this factory just sounds like dubstep. Imagine the "uhmm-chisss. crack-crack crack-crack" of ratcheting air guns in unlikely synchronicity with the bleeding of air valves and the beeping of forklifts. I'd bob my head, but someone might see me, and that'd be uncool.

My only professional interaction with people is negative. I'm a "quality inspector". I'm back to telling people they're doing shit wrong. I used to do that in the military. It comes naturally. I get it from my mom. Luckily, I'm good looking, or this job would be a lot harder. I get that from my dad.

Foam injected parts and assemblies criss-cross my inspection tables like a crowded Manila intersection. They're all little better than garbage to me. I fondle them. Eye them. Rate them. Send them back or pass them on. I'm 28 years old; I've been doing this for years in one form or another. Part #466Zsomething-something. Looks like a seahorse. Next.

I can't help but stop and think: someone, somewhere, is digging this stuff out of the ground. Does he ever look back at his hole and wonder when it will be empty?

I get the urge to tell people about my recent successes in photography all the time. Immediately, there's a voice from deep inside that bellows, "Nooboooodyeee caarrresss" in extended rebuff to my inclination to share. My only interaction with myself is negative.

It's lunch time and the beats in the factory have ceased. There's nothing like the absence of noise to reveal the cacophony that was. So clamorous it wasn't clamorous. So loud it was not-loud. The clamor has not been gone long enough to be forgotten. The stillness is like slowly vibrating air.

I don't need the quiet to hear myself think. I actually don't like thinking. I used to be able to not-think. You know how when women ask men what they're think-ing after a romp and men just want women to shut up? That was my brain: clear. An empty well with ponder-ous vibrations at the lip. I need this talent back.

I cut my hand climbing a tree yesterday: don't throw dog toys at trees. Today, I'm wearing a black medical glove to protect the gash: Luke Skywalker. The day goes by so much faster when you're thinking you're someone else. A worker cruises by on crutches. You've got to choose your alter egos wisely or they just be-come cumbersome.

I think I intimidate my boss. Which is made doubly weird because I also think he is a cleverly designed robot. If he were a cleverly designed robot, his timidity would be calculated. That would mean that I am predictable. If I'm predictable then you know how this story ends. You'll read on anyway. That makes the world a patronizing mess.

My mind snaps back to my computer terminal where I wrote tomorrow's date. "It's Wednesday". I mutter as I delete Friday from the entry. I feel as hopeless and deflated as a man watching his dog run into a busy street. The days are too slow. My weeks are so empty now.

Shoot. Empty isn't such a bad thing. An empty mind is called meditation. An empty inbox is bullshit free. One of my favorite things in the world is an echo, which happens in an empty space. The best fortune cookie I ever had was empty. What we need is to be able to appreciate a little emptiness. The spaces between thoughts.

This job is the space between adventures. Those diggers though; I'm of a mind to take this garbage in front of me and fill their empty spaces. I'll leave that impulse on the lip of the well while I pick blood out of my nose and wait for the dubstep to begin anew.

Window Pain | NakedThoughts #20

I like living downtown because I can walk my dog past restaurants and watch people eat. I try to figure out whether or not the couples that catch my eye are happy. There's a curious correlation between their happiness and my mood. If I am happy, they are happy. If I am something other than happy they are even happier. Today, like most days, I'm mellow and they are ecstatic.

Like the way casinos pump O2 into gaming halls to make people euphoric, and without inhibition there's something about restaurant glass that makes the people inside look more attractive to those on the inside. Not all restaurants can afford this trick. Near no one looks sexy eating at Taco Bell. Here at Matadors, everyone looks trendy and happy.

The dog pulls me past more windows. The sounds of today are the scratchy gravel-creek of loose concrete underfoot lubricated by rain and grime. Cars go by with an extra whoosh on the wet roads. Tommy is constantly forgetting that I just told him not to pull so there's a broken record playing my voice on top of it all. "Heel" I say, mostly to myself now. I can see my breath, but I'm not cold: my favorite temperature.

Dogs must think of leashes the way men think of condoms. If a leash is the price of going for a walk, then so be it. But they'd rather run free.

I think pharmaceutical companies have intentionally withheld the male contraceptive. There is already a significant population decline in the middle classes and above. It started in the early 80s, when men got smart about women in their baby crazy years; now referred to as the 'talent gap'. Anyway, there would be no babies. If there were a shot I could take, I'd put that needle straight up on the snooze button on my alarm and reload it every night.

'tis no such thing.

I wish people would say hello instead of greeting me with questions. I would say hello back and go on my (merry) way. Instead, they say, "How's it going?"
I'm inclined to knee jerk snippets of sass when my mind is on other things, such as getting by this person without engaging them: I reply, "Still breathing".
Then they laugh, but I don't laugh. I don't think it's funny.
Then they feel stupid.
Then I feel bad. But it doesn't show on my face. I am stoical.
Now, they think I'm an asshole.
In turn, I feel misunderstood, which makes me, finally, angry. Anger is the only emotion that shows on my face. Now I am being an asshole.

Then I walk away.

57

The dog and I are cruising again. I'm semi-stalking this girl I met while walking Tommy the other day, and he is sniffing ladies pockets like he's 5-0. What are the odds of running into her again? Romance is dead. I should just look her up on Fb. I won't though, I don't actually want to find her. That would be work, and I can't afford it.

When we pass small dogs walked by cute girls, I loudly ask Tommy if he would like to eat them; he's a Pitbull. Tommy seems too eager at the thought, and my face shows no emotion. Another missed connection hurries along.

Owning a dog in the city is like saying, "My need for companionship outweighs my distaste for picking up shit with my hands." That thought makes me wish I were in one of those restaurants. I'd ask for a seat facing the window so that I could see if the glass works both ways. No one is ever looking out the window at me when I'm standing there looking in. I always thought windows were for looking out, yet, I'm only ever on the outside looking in.

New York, New York 2014 | NakedThoughts #21

I was laying on my back in the grass; an opportunity you don't pass on in NYC. Rain was falling in sparse dustings. The drops felt like spring fighting the troughs of winter lashings. How many competing gusts brought the drops to terminus on my face?

Bryant Park is my favorite park in the city.
It is... cozy, somehow.

I was waiting for my train and contemplating missing its tenuous appointment for the intangible opportunity of an unexpected, untamed night. There are always whispers of adventure that float through the drafty streets of this city. It's a chemical blend of the exhaust, the exhaled breaths of a thousand, thousand people, the concrete dust kicked up by the wind, and a score of active aromas that curl and combust into sentience: the drifting life force of New York.

I was nearly asleep when this amalgamation of life snapped me from my musings.
The sky a violet, churning purple. My favorite sky; a sleepy royal vibration.

I stood, brushing grass from my hair, and looked straight down West 41st, like you are now. It was a rousing sight.

Eyes watery from yawning, colors blotched, and shapes converged like a rushing crowd of family and sailors eager to tell each other about their adventures. I blinked and the lines were straight again, the buildings quietly minding their own. The sun trumpeted its departure. I rushed to capture the final moments of its announcement.

A frozen photo of New York is an untrue vestige of the living, anomalous city.
To feel the heart of New York you need to see its colors run.

A cab driver raced for the next red light and the city passed indifferently while I stole light with a camera and mused about grass.

New York, NY. 2014

New York, New York 2014
This is the photo I captured that day.

Simmering | NakedThoughts #22

Have you ever thought that the granite countertop in your kitchen is frozen? I mean, everything has a melting point, and if magma is liquid rock, then granite is frozen rock. It's not exactly an enlightening thought, but it's what pinged my brain while I ate chocolate chip cookies with not frozen milk.

I first thought of this in high school when I, with absolute seriousness, mistakenly referred to ice as solid water. Mrs. Zimmerman laughed at me. I don't think I am any smarter than I was back then, only wiser for recognizing it.

This NakedThought actually began two hours ago while floating in an isolation tank, wondering how cold it would need to be to freeze water with a thousand pounds of salt in solution. All the while thankful the air and water were near perfectly heated.

The mind is an odd thing, and believing so implies that I am somehow apart from it. There is Me and there is my Mind.

In the isolation tank, the complete dark is somehow different when my eyes are open than when they are closed. Does floating in heated water on a timer constitute simmering? For a time, I kept pace with the old brag of my heart, "I am. I am. I am.", until, try as I might, I could no longer hear it. Now what?

I wanted to write while in the isolation tank, but the $50 per hour I was spending to lay in the super slick, warm bathwater, subverted my hunting for a pen. Instead, I wished for a sound activated voice recorder suctioned to the roof of the capsule. The luxuries of our day! My mind, unruly steward that it is, skipped tracks until the pin landed on Denzel Washington waving a voice recording pen in front of Jodi Foster in the movie, Inside Man. I wonder how many white people thought Denzel was a stupid name until he became famous.

An isolation chamber is also referred to as a sensory deprivation tank, and I think both are stupid names. I was acutely aware of how uncomfortable I constantly was, and I haven't felt isolated in a really long time; not even inside. I claimed, "I am, I am." alongside the rhythm of my heart until it halted its claim to being, and in the absence, I wondered if my Mind is the eternal companion of Me, like spinning stars trying to collide. Where repulsion is insanity (my mind left me), and oneness is when my Mind and I, frozen apart, heat to melting and become a single bright spot, enlightened. Then, after a moment that lasts forever, explode into the gases that make solid water and liquid steel, and a student that only matures enough to afford floating in salt solutions, and for the briefest of perceivable moments, almost thinks he can understand himself.

Arson | NakedThoughts #23

I'm on match(dot)com. It's not a real place, but you can meet people there. These dating sites are like the bad part of town. The part of town you commiserate about with your neighbors, but drive by every so often to remind yourself it's there. You despise it, but you also think you'd have the nicest house on the block if you stooped to investing in the market.

Tinder is another suburb like Match. I drive through Tinder often. It's more accessible and the real-estate is easier to produce. I feel like Tinder is my relapse into dating. The Nicorette gum to my emotional woman addiction; I'm always ready to quit, but I never do.

Lately, I drive by the Tinder block on the way home from the school where I teach. I've been so many things this year; now I work in special education. The Special Ed teachers at the schools where I teach say I'm a 'silent force.' They think I'm strong, and stern, and willful. They think I'm patient! People really only see what they are primed to see. If you tell someone that you're going to do a magic trick, they are already halfway to believing that you've done what you're going to do before you've begun doing it. This works on kids because they want to believe in magic, and teachers because they want to believe in the help. If you boiled all the shiny impurities out of my personality, you'd find that I'm really scatter-brained and absentminded: faux patience. I can wait for little Johnny to figure out whose head his hat belongs on because my mind isn't really there either.

I'm a functioning retard.

All of the above is true, until a woman creeps into my special, secured, upper class part of town. When I inhale that sweet blend of herbal shampoo mixed with vegetarian cleansed yoga sweat, and discover that that aroma was meant for me.... Well, that's like dropping a magnet into a dish of iron shavings. All the poles in my scattered brain align and I go from absentminded to dogged. I consume her like a full serving of Chinese food after a fast. Take the bone away, and I'm all whimpers and pouty eyes. At least until the magnetism fades.
Either way, I find the experience as dissatisfying as breaking the last match in the tinder box on the strike paper. Had I a sentimental bone in my body, I'd have enough of those match heads for a respectable arson project. Only, there are too many houses to burn in the dating district, and I don't want to walk in to light the flame.

Beach Park | NakedThoughts #24

I'm at a beach park. It smells like weed because: Washington. I really didn't expect anyone to be here. This expectation is more a result of my own solitary nature than anything based in reality; it's a beautiful day. I recently taught a mentally-retarded kid how to say "it's a beautiful day" in Japanese. It might be the only thing he'll remember of me for the rest of his life. Anyway, MR doesn't mean stupid. Stupid is arriving at a park on a sunny day and being stunned because it's packed.

I found an empty table with a little bit of shaded sun near the trash cans because, you know, misery loves company. There's a pasty goth chick with long oily hair sitting alone a few dozen yards from me in a chair brought from home. Ever wonder what those goths you grew up with turned out like when they hit their middle years? They look the same. You just notice them less. Is she like me, alone in a park full of people having fun? Nope. She just shoed away what looks to be a future young goth so she could toke up in peace.

The sounds of today are the irregular thumping of balls hitting the ground. Ever wonder what happened to those kids who couldn't catch a ball in high school? They still play with each other and their kids can't catch either. Repeated apologies sound from the kid whose volleyball spends as much time rolling toward my table as it does flying through the air. People talk soundlessly in the distance, waving hands and pointing and such. The collated hum of their voices are drowned by the sound of the highway bouncing across the lake.

A girl and a boy blow bubbles from their picnic table and chase them across the grass. They always return to the table to blow more bubbles. I try to focus on the bursting sound of the bigger bubbles. If I could only isolate that one sound from the cacophony, the world would be a better place. I know it, somehow. I stare pretty hard here; anyone who catches me staring will probably think I hate those kids. I have permanent hate-face.

I quit Facebook today. I literally decided just now, this moment. The invisible lines that connect people around the world tie together to make a snare. I snared a rabbit in arctic survival school. Instead of the wire strangling it or snapping its neck, the rabbit's heart exploded in its chest from fear and panic. For me, that snare catches my time and a piece of my soul. Like an urban bird surrounded by picnicking people, I'm starving for a connection with over 15,000 friends and fans online. I realized just now that the one thing Facebook has been distracting me from is loneliness. The only thing worse than being lonely is pretending that you are not.

Ever wonder what happened to the loner kid you grew up with who never hung out with anyone? He sits in a park people-watching, alone, wishing he could punt some kid's volleyball into the lake because being angry makes him happy.

Adventurous | NakedThoughts #25

I try to visit different Starbucks when I go "out". It makes me feel adventurous.
The varying looks of concentration on peoples' faces could make an interesting photo book. You know, one of the books you flip through at Barnes and Noble and never buy. Barnes and Noble are the only real collectors of books these days.

I'm writing a few books now. I went from zero to four in three months. Four unfinished dialogs about myself. I think I want extra sharp paper edges so that my writing will leave a mark on book browsers. Three of them won't have pictures, so there's not much potential for paper cutting heartless leafers-through of books.

A pair of old ladies can't find a table. I tell them they can sit with me, and one is surprised and grateful. I tell her it's a European thing, "Smaller bubbles". I explain simply. They pick up their jackets and leave.

The sounds of today are the hums of aimless conversations barely audible over the Opeth blasting in my headphones and the quiet voice in my head, telling me that I'm supposed to be "working". Whatever that entails.

I try to find a place in each Starbucks that is out of view of most patrons. People watching is so distracting.

I spent a solid three minutes staring at a safari scene pasted to the back of a woman's laptop, imagining a trip to Africa.
Ah • free • kà
Ah • freak • ā

I wonder if this woman is a freak. Her swimming expressions say she's kinda crazy; emotional at least. Whatever she's working on is certainly dramatic. Maybe she's a writer, too...

...Her character falls through time and reality whenever her heart beat rises too high, like the Hulk meets the Accidental Time Machine in a gamma-ray faraday cage. Fall in love, jump into another reality. Trip on Lego dinosaurs, and zip into the future. Thunder... keep calm or find yourself next to alien Indiana Jones riding a ball of lighting down an extinct NYC volcano. This will be book five. I'll never complete it.

I just realized that she's wearing a woven blanket with a hole in the middle for her head. Fashion. Either she's out of time, or I spend too much time in my loft, alone, with unfinished ideas and alcohol.

Two guys in suits make elaborate gestures to make up for the lackluster of their PowerPoint. Salesmanship. A man with a ponytail looks like an ugly woman. I looked twice. A Chinese guy in a top hat looks lost; builds a table fort out of folders and books.

"If you find yourself lost in the woods… fuck-it! Build a house!" - Mitch Hedberg.

Someone vacated a nook for me. My day can begin.

The girl in front of me is watching Sponge Bob on her laptop. Sponge Bob is waving his arms about and bubbles seem to mime the closed captions I can only half-read over her shoulder. She's probably seventeen years old. I'm probably supposed to call her down since I'm her substitute teacher. But, all things being equal and transparent; she probably cares less for my position than I do, I just want to get through the day, and I suppose that's all she wants, too. Authority is relative.

The sounds of today are the nearly silent plunging of keys on twenty-seven Yamaha pianos by twenty-seven students with two hundred and seventy fingers. With headphones donned they seem to mime to their sheet music. Twenty-seven students and one watching Sponge Bob. It all sounds like clothed mallets beating on useless textbooks. It all sounds like a headboard beating against the bedroom wall two doors down the hall in the early afternoon. There's some semblance of rhythm but everyone's doing their own thing and it sounds awkward.

When I taught special-ed, I learned that I had to physically restrain children who had no concept of authority. I would hold Alex-the-horrible-smelling-destroyer at his desk until he was reminded of what a boundary was and who was boss. This usually took thirty to forty-five minutes every day. Authority is a flat currency based on fear, respect, and pain. Everything else is a derivative.

Five students have white bands tied around their heads. "Vote for…" this shmuck or that. Class elections. They don't know it yet but they're really selecting their favorite person to blame for this year's problems. Shit, it took me over a decade to finally get it. Had I known then, maybe I would have voted. When I was in Tech School in the Air Force I was "Red Rope", the highest ranked student by appointment. I was the instructors' favorite person to blame for everything my 300+ airmen did wrong. Authority is punitive.

In third period I stood for the Pledge of Allegiance. I had eighteen students and I could barely hear the words over their eighteen flapping mouths. My eye started twitching then. I probably should have called them all down, but I am substitute authority and just wanted to get through the day.

There are four minutes left in class.

Africa Lounge | NakedThoughts #27

I'm sitting in Africa Lounge, an ironically named bar in Seattle airport. NakedThoughts began in an airport. There was an old man, a purple-haired waitress, a pulled-pork sandwich, and people riding scooters through the airport. There's none of that sort of character here. My waitress is Hispanic and thumbs her chin thoughtfully while people order. There are no pensive old men, and Americans are too uptight to ride scooters with nonchalance through the airport.

I didn't want to check a bag, so I'm wearing all my layers to winter in NY for Christmas. Undressing in this close space feels like an awkward dance, and more than a few people watch me. My eyes pull up sharply from my fries as someone exclaims, "Are you a Muslim?!". I don't know what I expected to see when I found the voice, but it's just a bunch of white people getting on about something. I probably heard them wrong. Boring.

Children flee their parents down the corridor outside the bar. They look back to ensure pursuit before trumpeting down the hall again. A group of black guys peer into the restaurant and move on. This place should be called South Africa Lounge.

The sounds of today are the din of conversation punctuated by the shuffling of ice in the cups of the couple behind me. Some guy is telling a table full of strangers about karate. He's a brown belt, and his voice cuts through the crowd like an actual karate-chop. The table is a circle-jerk of "about me's", and he's taking way too long to get it all out. Airport announcements cut him off, and as I let my gaze drift, I lock eyes with a husband whose wife I've caught eyeing me twice. He has too, apparently. However, my face is stormy as I inwardly contend with a vice-like headache that is begging me to put this phone away. I stare daggers through his eyes and imagine the back of his head exploding from the pressure building inside mine. He drops his eyes; I've still got it. No miscommunication here.

Wouldn't you know it; they're calling my flight, and my waitress is MIA. My mental tip counter is like an analog counter on a bomb spinning to zero. I've resorted to holding my money and receipt in the air like a student with a flag.

When I was finishing my PMP, I took an entire class on communication. Did you know that there are 108 channels of communication to the lead sponsor of a project or something like that? It doesn't matter. That means there are likely a dozen other ways I could reach my waitress, or the people at the table could tell the brown belt to STFU, or I could get the people behind me to stop dicing with their ice cups. But... its late and I have a headache, so I'm going to ignore the ice people, stare daggers at the husband, and wave money in the air like South Africa Lounge is a strip club.

Party City | NakedThoughts #28

I'm at Party City and it hasn't even opened yet. It's Tuesday morning and, in lieu of figuring out my own life, I'm overlording child labor.

Among the many things that bother me about this store, one is the florescent lighting. The lights are an alternating slum-gutter yellow with the occasional white tube illuminating the chaos of each isle.

Angel can't figure out where the chrome-plastic baseball trophy goes. I want to tell him that no one deserves trophies in baseball, but it will invariably go over his head. Angel and Melissa are my child labor underlings. They are 16-18-year-old special-needs students learning to work in the real world. We will spend the wee hours of this morning practicing job applications after we tidy up Party City. I'm 30 years old and still can't get a resume right, so I will feel for Angel when, while filling out his emergency contacts, he can't figure out that his mother's name, Brenda, starts with a B. I don't even have an emergency contact.

The sounds of Party City are a confusing mix of Christmas tunes and depressing Country music. It's mid-January. The sounds of crumpling and crunching plastic wrappers are the notes of a disorganized aisle coming together. And... that's about it. The mall is opening, and I'm sure this lack of bluster is blissful to the employees at Party City. It is to me.

I just had a sword fight with Angel, and his smile is everything. He's not a hair taller than 5', with short arms to boot. If he noticed my reach outstripping his by two feet or more, he didn't bat an eye. He charged. There's a warrior buried in that kid somewhere. They say these little people with missing chromosomes are stronger than the average person, and I flinch a little bit when he puts his head down and fakes a charge. Well, it's always brains over brawn, and my tube of Avengers: Ultron wrapping paper beat his ninja-hands three times of three.

There's an "Almost Funny" category in the greeting card section. I feel like these are the cards of life. I pick up a card depicting a yawning cat surrounded by fireworks. It stares me in the eye while American Pie plays through the ceiling speakers. I yawn, causing my eyes to water, because the cat on the card is yawning, and an old lady does a double take as she walks by, because it looks like I'm crying. Crying alone in an obtuse aisle of Party City, holding an empty basket and a blank greeting card. Who is going to help me adjust to the real world?

Solitaire | NakedThoughts #29

There is an elderly lady sitting next to me and I could write an entire page about her. I'll refrain. Just imagine your happily portly grandma traveling alone in the friendly skies, asking a nice gentleman like myself to hold her iPad until she's ready to play her solitaire. Single suit. Spades. Flying is something altogether itself, isn't it?

Three rows in front of me an abrupt flight attendant is playing a game of shuffle with a couple and their infant child because they can't sit in an exit row. Makes sense, but you can tell it's her last shift.

The lady next to me is watching all her solitaire cards spiral and fly about in victory. I've always thought there were way too many cards in that display. But her phone rang, an old lady ring tone, and I ended up watching the end of that victory charade while she fished for her phone. How'd she play that so fast?

The sounds of tonight are the quiet din of private conversations, and the muted animation on the phone of the guy next to me. His headphones are on, but I peep at his screen and know the show, so I hear the action anyway. I briefly look up from writing to watch the flight attendant mime safety procedures. I swivel my head to see the rest of the cabin, not a single other head is raised to watch. The pilot promises turbulence on our flight and still, no one raises a brow. The nice lady next to me must know she isn't making it out of this plane if it goes down, and refuses to spare a bit of her attention from the game. Is that a new one already?! At least she's got the window seat. I won't have to climb over her in the event of a water "landing".

I forewarned the guy next to me that I'll be disrupting his sleep to hit the head. Now that is airplane etiquette.

The baby that was moved attempts to drown out the drone of turbine engines as we taxi; its wails punctuated with coughs as though the cries impatiently waiting to wiggle its tonsils are shoving each other to get out. I feel nothing.

Perhaps babies wail on planes because they are afraid the louder noise will get more attention?

As the weight of our ascent presses me deeper into the seat I realize the bright, blue-green light of the solitaire table has gone out. She's looking out the window. Watching the world pass her by, I imagine. That's what I feel looking out that window at a dark, sparsely twinkling landscape. But, if I played solitaire game after game, knowing I would win every time and the winning would be easy, I suppose I'd be watching the world with a mind of met expectation. All the things I need would be out there, they just need to be put in the right order.

The lady's returned to her game, and I'm writing on the toilet. As I see it, I'm fulfilling a promise, and promises are one small thing to keep in order in life. Oddly, this is the most comfortable seat on this plane.

I'll have to go back to my own seat, 23E, eventually, and I've resigned myself to watching her play solitaire on my right and the guy on my left watch Oceans 12 for the rest of the night.

Waiting on the pilots' promised excitements, I think to myself that I might be the turbulence in other people's lives.

I inwardly curse the seat in front of me for reclining and recline my own in retribution.

My eyes hurt.

*End Note

The old lady hands me her coke to hold while she fishes through her tablet for a photo of the granddaughter she's trying to sell me after having learned that I am a writer. I'd really like a sip of coke.

I thought about giving her this to read.

Interlude

After setting my last NakedThought aside and giving the nice lady her cup of coke back, I set myself to doing the final edits on "A Knight". It is a Dream Dagger that I'm planning to include in the first volume of Dream Daggers & Imaginary Friends. She sips her coke and insists on telling me how she has read three books each week since she was fifteen years old. I so badly want to ask her age but as she puts it, "I've read A LOT of books! A lot."

The filter I ignore when I write a naked thought kicks in and urges me to let her read this story. So, I turn the brightness up on my screen until it seems as though I am unleashing the sun, I increase the font size to 'elderly', and hand over my laptop.

I'm feeling a little misled at the moment, because reading three books a week for the thousand-odd years she's been alive suggests to me that she'd be a fast reader. Her eyes should be eating up the page. Instead she's pointing her finger at the screen and I can see her mouth working inaudibly as she crawls through the text.

After receiving my computer back, I apparently earn a story in return: her grandson, who is transgender, (and while she is completely accepting, she often forgets to refer to him as a female), "plays Dungeons and Dragons and people let him -her- tell them what to do." It turns out she really likes that game, and loves stories like it. I also learn about her father's entire military history, and that of her brother-in-law who was an intelligence officer.

There is no comment about the story she read.

Flying really is something else.

The Buffet Line | NakedThoughts #30

This horrid woman hasn't handed me a single serving spoon, even though I've followed her through half a dozen serving plates in this buffet. I'm not a nice person, but I believe in manners, damnit.

She looks like Ursula granted herself some legs so she could come to this resort and eat chicken-fried rice.

There are no chickens in the ocean. Odd that. What is the chicken of the ocean?

I'm in Thailand.
Phuket... Poō•keht

This place is beautiful, but there is something wrong here. It is as though "Good Enough" is just a little too difficult anymore, and everything has been left to a slow descent toward entropy.

The sounds of today are the yelling of a grandmother throwing her voice across the buffet at a screaming toddler... in Chinese. I can hear waves crash when I focus on the water. The wind, just a hair stronger than a gentle breeze, seems to swirl in my ears after tracing the lines of my face. Oh, what it would be like to be the wind.

I want to move closer to those sounds, away from the clamor of this buffet and the cacophony of a third world country, but those sounds are in the sun, and the sun has already oppressed me this trip. My skin peels as if it's been burned by a nuclear flash in the sky. Which, technically, it has.

I spilled syrup on my page.

Every body is a beach body, unfortunately. I have to be careful which ones I look at, though. I'm here with a lady. Maybe I can look if I look for one of my friends, though. Not for me. Never for me. For a friend.

I saw a Japanese guy with a tramp spam that read "for belief" in Serif font. Blackmoor LET, I believe. I just spent seven minutes crawling through fonts on the Internet.

Anyway, I couldn't stop staring… but that is different, I think.
A rail-thin man with a lemur clinging to his forearm just passed us on the beach. My girlfriend's eyes have filled with tears. Unconditional love? Lust? Concern? Outrage? It's hard to tell what she's feeling until she speaks. Whatever I say will be the wrong thing… I hold my tongue and remember to keep my head on a swivel lest my eyes linger too long somewhere.

My eyes most quickly avert from old men in water-underwear. Do they possess uncanny courage (or lack

American fear), or is there an age at which I won't give a shit anymore? How do I get there? I'm only 31, but there's a fast track and a "hack" for everything, these days.

As I look around the beach I keep trying to match the women I accidentally see with one my friends, but it's difficult because I don't have any friends.
Perhaps I should go speak to someone?
I'll ask Ursula what her problem is...

Interlude

I just got in so much trouble for writing that bit about checking women out for my imaginary friends. I came to the sunny, sweaty, stinky, beautiful land of beaches, rainforest, counterfeit wares, and garbage, for my girl-friend. Thailand was never on my list of economies to drop thousands of dollars into. Still, if looks that could slay men also caused collateral damage, half the beach would be strewn with bodies now. Some jokes you just can't make. Some jokes you just have to make. Yet, there are some laws of love that can't be escaped no matter how much affection you put in the rainy-day cookie jar.

Big Foot | NakedThoughts #31

Whenever I instinctively don't like a person, I try to find something to compliment them on. I rarely give this compliment; I just act the exchange out in my head and keep those good deed endorphins for myself.

The person next to me just sat absurdly close. The unwelcome breach of my bubble was placated by an intoxicating perfume. I could see long red hair out of the corner of my eye. I turned with an eager smile the way a dog who just heard his bowl filled comes bounding around the corner. She flipped her hair obnoxiously, revealing a man. I should have known; I'm in the Philippines. Now I'm pissed; my bowl is empty, and I just wasted a smile. I don't have too many of those to give away. I feel extorted, tricked, confused. I still like her hair, but I'm keeping that to myself as I unceremoniously restore my bubble's volume. I'm tired of being gawked at by old ladies and lady-boys. I am quietly apologizing to every woman I've offended with an intense stare, as I feel myself mentally undressed by the red-haired man/woman who has now moved back into my bubble.

Last call for my plane. I always wait for the herd of people waiting to board to slim before I attempt boarding, myself. All the mooing and the shuffling while waiting for the plane to ingest its passengers; I skip that. The eyes that don't meet, and the noses that pretend nothing offends them; I skip that. This plane can't eat us cattle fast enough.

I'm boarding an Emirates flight to Dubai. That, in my escape from Filipinos, is something akin to two steps forward and one back. Many Filipinos work in the Emirates to send money back home. I am half Filipino. That makes other Filipinos want to celebrate, for some reason. They want to know where I'm from. What languages I speak. What I want to eat. If I am single. Then mothers and grandmothers offer up their daughters like sacrifices on an altar.

Ironically, I'm headed to Dubai for work, too. Going to make that "big sale." The pessimist in me says I'm just headed toward getting my next failure out of the way. The optimist in me says I probably won't get the sale because I'm too pessimistic.

I've been upgraded to Business Class on Emirates. I'd like to say it was my smile that earned it, but we know I wasted my good one already. The guy next to me has also been upgraded to Business class, though not by a chance overbooking, like me. His insurance company gave him a sympathetic high five. His left foot is as large as his head and as shiny as his face. "Man! Mosquitos suck." He says after a fashion. Apparently, he's having some rare allergic reaction to nature. I'd have given up on the Philippines had something like that happened to me. This is his second round. Fool me once...

He got married in the Philippines but now his 'wife' won't leave without her mother and family. I ask if she's really worth the trouble. By his expression I can already tell our relationship is going downhill.

We are on our way to Dubai. I'm on my way to see a man about a horse, and sell him some pictures. Jason Matias, "international man of business." More like Evel Knievel puddle hopping blind. For Knievel, people paid to be there when he crashed. It was kinda like playing the lotto or rooting for a gladiator. It's the same for me. The odds as to whether or not this career has any legs are long, and I'm on the wrong side of the wager, but I'm going anyway. If I don't fail while daring greatly, then I fail for no reason, and who wants to listen to that story?

The sounds of today are the constant mechanical wind of that airplane vent you can't turn off. I make a grass flute out of two pieces of paper, but Big Foot asks me to stop. It probably sounds like his wife's voice, I muse. I hear Arabic, Tagalog, English, and something that might be English, only, most of the words are missing. I order whiskey, straight, no rocks, no nonsense.

I've got nothing to complain about. Business class on Emirates feels like success. I try to imagine what success looks like for me in the future as I press buttons here and there in this amazing personal space. I haven't earned a career win yet, and I know it. So, I keep those visions of the future to my innermost self, and borrow endorphins against a future of success.

An Army of Ones | NakedThoughts #32

Thai massages are, like, ten dollars.

Before coming here (Phuket), a friend of mine insisted that I get a massage every day because "they're like a dollar". But a massage in Thailand is not one dollar, it's ten times that.

So, every time I get a massage, I am forced to think about this person's "one dollar".

Perhaps, "They're, like, a dollar..." was just a flippant generalization, or this person is terrible at exchanging currencies in their head. But maybe a dollar doesn't mean to them what it means to me. That's what's really been bothering me.
Their dollars vs my dollars.

Ten dollars will never be the same as one dollar in my mind. They're just too hard won to be thrown into a crowd and considered as one. The forest will always be a forest of trees to me, and my bank account will always be comprised of an army of ones.

I'm thinking of Thai massages right now because, even though I'm staring out the window at a very Thai monsoon, I can still feel the soles of my feet aching with the memory of shopping at the Night Market. I'd really like a "one dollar" Thai foot massage right now. Even if that means going out into the rain.

Yesterday, or was it two yesterday's ago, it's hard to tell with how little I sleep... I went to Night Market. At Night Market, you rub sweaty elbows with hundreds of people from dozens of countries while scrutinizing counterfeit goods to proudly display as souvenirs to your friends.

When you need a break from that, you find the food market where you look for that one vendor with the crickets. You take pictures of seasoned crickets and eat one or two seasoned crickets so that you can tell your friends that you ate crickets and are thus, really "doing Thailand".
They're gross, btw.

Then you realize that the body odor you've been nurturing in the Thai sweat-market has been supplanted by that of not-quite-dead fish, fried duck, burnt seasoning, and tasty dumplings. So... you head back into the maze of shops to regain familiar territory.

The sounds of Night Market are indistinct waves of noise. A garbling cluster-fuck of predators and prey in a discount-market environment. I can't figure out which I am; predator or prey. Angelina is hunting for Louie V; I am protectively hiding my wallet. There are half a dozen languages of the Eastern European variety all spoken in broken English with enterprising Thai.

The younger Thai give off a vibe like, I'm just here because I have to be. The older Thai give a vibe like, I'm here because I need to be. Learn from your elders or become them.

I watched a 1%-er give a talk about pitchforks and peasants once. In a nut-shell, they'll come with pitchforks if we, the people at the top of the food chain, don't change our ways. Then, he made an interesting comparison. If he were born in a low place with dirt roads and cow-pulled sleds, i.e. without privilege, instead of becoming a captain of industry, his enterprise might have been selling fruit on the side of a dusty road.

If that were me, would I even have a fruit basket? Where on the scale of things would I sit between the young Thai and the old Thai. What would a dollar be worth to me then?

You realize, if you're keen, that the market is a sham. An ingenious one. It's really just a few big department stores divided into scores of store fronts and scattered throughout a maze. If you are on the fence about a purchase, you'll see it again and again, enough times to finally buy it. It's a physical marketing funnel disguised as an amusement.

There are a few gems; just a few. If there were too many, there would be no gems.

Thinking of the hours spent shopping for fake Louis V with my girlfriend makes me think of massages, and the weight of my wallet, and whether or not it's worth going out in the rain.

Testing Testing | NakedThoughts #33

I'm sitting in the corner of a cafeteria next to an old, bald guy. I can't really see him because the morning sun is ruining my right eye. I'm facing east. I picked this spot so I could look out the window, but I think the plan has backfired. I'm stuck looking at the fifty other tired faces who showed up to take this test instead.

It's a "chemistry-math-equations" exam as described by King County. We're all testing for a handful of positions with the Board of Water.

I don't fit in here with this crowd. It's just a feeling. I haven't had a boss in five years. I don't really need a 9-5 but the insecurity of creative entrepreneurship is like having a penis-shaped tree in your front lawn. It's an eyesore, but it makes the neighbors uncomfortable, and for that, it's worth it. All the people who think I can't do this thing or that, or that what I want to do with my life is a fairytale- those are my neighbors. It used to be my family, but I think they're on my side now, so that's something.

But, if I did get a j-o-b, this job would be okay. It is 4 days working, followed by 4 days off. So, I'm technically only working half of a year. For that, I think I'll ace the math on this exam. Working half the year would allow me to work the other half on my own stuff. Photography and writing, and sometimes staring at an unchanging computer screen. Also, managing my life in general, which seems to be extra-cumbersome.

I can kinda make out a goatee on this guy sitting next to me. He's the quiet type, which is good. I normally spend the nine o'clock hour battling my inane instinct to stay in bed. It's a daily 90-minute conflict. Today it was followed by a chocolate donut and a glass of milk. I drink milk from my whiskey glasses; they have the widest mouth for dunking, while not being too deep and requiring an over commitment of milk.

Five minutes to testing.

The sounds of this cafeteria are the mumbles of too-early conversation on safe subjects. The weather. The test. Job hunting.

The test proctor, a rotund woman with a squeaky voice, is throwing test packets at tables now. Will she sing when I finish the exam?

"Take a deep breath. It's just questions on a piece of paper." she tells the crowd.

-lady, do you know how smart I am? (how smart I hope I am).

Do I really want to pass this exam, or am I just here to say that I tried?

97

Despite feeling smart, I have to put my glasses on anyway. Look smart, feel smart... be smart? If looks and feelings = reality, the world would be a fucked up place.

My phone is in airplane mode; not so that I don't cheat, but so that I don't get on social media.

105 questions. 105 chances to make right decisions in 2 hours. If I could make this many right decisions in a row I don't think I'd be here. 105 chances for regret.

Thoughts during the exam:
Question 8: shit...
Q11: Does the "just pick C rule" still apply when you're 30?
Q11a: Since the day I became an asshole teenager, test taking has made me automatically want to do two things and one of them is: take a shit. Do I dare get up so early in the exam?
Q14: Ooooh- tricky
Q17: I'm a dumbass
Q21: 20% done with the test and ninety minutes left. Better hurry up.
Q27: hmmm... I averaged $50/hr this month. Why am I here again?
Q28: Oooo...Science
Q29: The test is wrong! Do I raise a stink or look past it?
Q37: The heavy sighs of the guy next to me....
Q44: Damn- I don't know this stuff

Q52: I've been anticipating being half-way done for the last hour. Now that I've arrived… It's anticlimactic

Q77: Is myopia a brain disease? (edit: it's definitely not)

Q93: I hope this old dude does his own laundry. He's been coughing into that shirt for two hours.

Q105. Done. 35 minutes to spare. Do I:

    A) check my answers or,

    B) leave

Answer: (B), before this guy gets me sick.

My corner seat turned out kinda nice now that Seattle remembered what part of the world it belongs to and ushered in a blanket of rain clouds. At least I could see.

The fat lady didn't sing when I handed in my test, but she was cheerfully marking X's on people's exams and her headphones were really loud.

Expectation, meet reality.

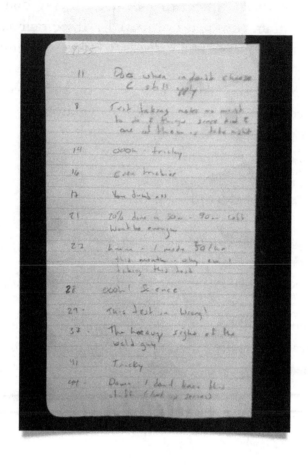

my faded notes from the day of the test

Judgementality | NakedThoughts #34

I am on the subway in NYC. Ever look at someone with contempt for absolutely no reason? Well, no reason other than that they look contemptible. Such a person just strolled past me in a tweed suit, high water pants showing shoes more expensive than everything I'm carrying (including my computer), and shaded glasses. Not sun-shaded; just rose-colored enough to make me hate him. I'm not jealous of his money in the sort of way that makes you hate a person, I'm just contemptuous of how he uses it... and everything else about him.

People Watching 2.0 is going a step beyond casual judgementality, to trying to read their phones. Close proximity, high-risk People Watching. I was all about that life the last time I was here. I still am, it's not a perishable skill as long as your eyes work. However, I realize that I have just matured to People Watching 3.0: acquiring book recommendations from people on the subway.

The woman next to me is on people watching 2.0 still. Part of achieving 3.0 is acquiring people watching 2.5; avoiding other people looking at your own phone. It's a situational awareness thing. I'm ducking her right now. It's all in the wrist. These big phone screens don't make it easy.

She's reading "Men Explain Things to Me," It's a skinny little thing. It's probably a text on the feminist agenda that belittles men for not being women. Or maybe it's so skinny because the author doesn't have much praise for the deductive ability of people like me. People with penises.

The guy with the glasses got off the train immediately. I think he felt the vibe.
I'm walking around Columbus Circle now. A new building is materializing in front of me. If buildings had personalities, I wonder if the gleaming new skyscrapers feel like the guy in tweed; all shiny and tall, and flaunting their bullshit with their noses turned up, not realizing that it's the old-timers that made all these things possible for them. It's different though; I'd hang out with the new building. I like new stuff.

I know it's only 10am, but I'm itching for an overpriced hot dog. I withdrew $100 specifically for street food. I already spent $12.75 on Chinese food, 1am.

The city sings. If you squint your ears to make the sounds blend the same way you squint your eyes to make colors run together, you can hear it.

Damn this gyro smells good.

The sounds of today are the beating drums of construction equipment. The swish-swish of people dragging their feet. They are silent; of course 80% of them have

102

headphones on, ignoring the music of the city. Their faces sometimes make me concerned about what they are listening to. A Taiwanese woman is cleaning the doorway to her restaurant with a boiling teapot she purchased on the set of Disney's Aladdin. I'm not sure how to describe that sound, but the heat washed over me momentarily. If there is a chorus, it is sung by construction workers talking about their family and girlfriend problems. I don't see many female construction workers. I don't hear many arguments complaining about that. The city is all bass today.

I spend a lot of time thinking about how I hate my life, but I must care about it a little bit: I still lower my phone when I cross the street. I try to put a body or two between my own and oncoming traffic. Today that body was a janitor, pushing a cart full of recyclables. I said a belated "Good Morning" to him, and he looked at me as if I were wearing tweed. He's right; how do I know what kind of morning it is.

On Love | NakedThoughts #35

There's something about being outside that makes you think about what's inside. It's like, the space around you is too immense to consider, so you retreat into yourself.

I mean- the level of detail in reality is confounding. Even if we ignore the super massiveness of the universe and the incredible minutia of the subatomic realms, and consider the tangible world around us... I mean- did you know that General Sherman, the tree, has four billion leaves? Four. Billion. There's so much to take in. Even the tangible world is impossible to visualize.

Anyway, I am raking leaves, right now.
I retreat out of doors when I'm stressed, and nothing stresses me like love.
Love; it's as simple as a quark and has four billion leaves.

Spring cleaning is cleaning up winter's leavings, aka, the things you left in last autumn. It's the worst. I feel like life is forever a process of sorting the crises of the past. I began this NakedThought two seasons ago. Autumn. I was doing the leaves then, too.

The rake is making a grating sound that I don't think my relationship with life can handle. Yet, I need it. There's a fair breeze carrying noises that nature is using to mock me. The branches above me ruffle their dry leaves, and a modest creek fills the spaces between it all. I shut it out; it's too much, all this mocking tranquility. It's a veil that hides the overwhelming intricacy of existence. For instance, maple leaves, if left alone, decompose into a beautiful lace before vanishing completely and there are two people whose lives are colliding in an apartment beneath these trees that the wind and a forest full of gliding leaves just 'happen' around and nothing really matters. Only: it all does, there's just no reason for it.

Breathe

Calm is a space encircled by the high walls of meditation. At the very 1st degree of that encircling wall, meditation is attained by a clear mind. Right next to it, at the very last degree, meditation is achieved through cacophony.

So I rake. That vibration of springy, flat metal meeting grass, dry flora, concrete, and gravel connects my insides to the outside. My inner ear can't process this physical static. Chaos on the outside balances that on the inside. Clarity.

Dammit, I just realized that it is autumn again. The mess I twice cleared is a mess again, and I can't figure out if this is a problem or if this just: is. I have a new rake this year. Plastic, this time. It is wider and it makes less noise, so I rake twice as hard and listen four times more intently than that so that I can find that clarity. The grinding, the raking, the outdoors, the sweat, the mocking stream, the storm inside.... I broke the rake.

There's an Icelandic poem about a person whose life is in perpetual autumn.
As if Autumn is some sort of milestone. Every year this person ends up here and checks in with their heart. Am I where I meant to be? Is all "this" meant for me?

I'm back at it again. It's been a whole year since these thoughts started driving me outside. I have a leaf blower now. It is wonderfully noisy. Sometimes, I even look forward to being out here.

Anyway, love is a lot easier when you don't think about it.

I Am | NakedThoughts #36

I can hear my heart beat inside my head like the ticking of a clock. If there were a clock in my head, like everything else in there, it'd be broken. I estimate it's about 25% too fast. It's as if the subconscious mind that runs this meat machine is tired of my shit, and is pressing fast forward. Remember old VCRs?

I woke up sick.

Or, I should say, my body is sick. I've been looking into meditation and LSD lately. These two kinda go together... like puzzle pieces that are part of the same picture on the grander tapestry of the mind. LSD is the puzzle piece that would be annoying if lost, but it wouldn't ruin the experience. However, include that colorful, little jagged tile, and the tapestry is taken to new heights.

I've never done any hard drugs. Partially because I'm afraid of dying, but also because there's someone inside that I'm afraid of rediscovering. Do you have an old friend, the memory of whom is crisp and well defined? So vividly remembered that you don't actually care to catch up with him. You might even avoid "liking" a social media post for fear of striking up a conversation with said person. A past self is one such individual, and he's still lurking deep in my mind. I feel him come out of his apartment in the back of my head to peer down the hall and through my mind's eye sometimes. He scoffs at the brightness of my newish world, but I know he's waiting for an excuse to catch-up.

LSD is supposed to open all the doors of perception and, like a fire alarm, evacuate the residents of my mind into the cold dark; then burn down the building to keep them warm.

I've been meditating to prepare for this shredding of the ego so that I can coral all these versions of me, like a kindergarten teacher herding special-ed students during a fire-drill, so that we may have a safe, unified experience. I wonder how many selves rent an apartment in my head. There's a theory that all thought is universal, and your mind attunes to a tributary of consciousness split from an infinite, shared ocean of thought. When I meditate, I imagine rowing on that blue tributary, itself infinite, against the tide and away from the flow of my thoughts. I flee from those thoughts in search of the Me that is undefined by experience and free from expectation. He's the building manager who's not afraid of my bad tenants, the one who's boat doesn't rock when the river gets rough. That guy; the original, authentic Me, probably doesn't define his day by the sickness he woke with (one hour before his damn alarm) but simply opens his eyes and thinks: I Am.

this is the place I visualize when I row at the gym. side note - I also listen to death metal while I row.

I'm about to sleep with a woman. She knows it because it's been arranged. Kinda like an Indian wedding except we both know Bollywood isn't going throw a parade tonight. She has to go home to drug her sick cat before too long, anyway.

I make it my goal to make her late for this because if she does stay in spite of her obligations, I'll feel like I've won a small victory. Then I'll get to draw myself a trophy in the steam from the scalding shower I'll take later. I'm a millennial; we all deserve awards according to the parents that hate our generation, because we grew up being awarded for mediocrity.

I just got another dating-app match and this one wants me to come to Miami. Talk about moving fast. I'll probably talk to her later because I have a void to fill, but for now, I need to engineer the relationship rollercoaster in front of me because the night will only be as good as the first drop is high.

My friend Mike just texted me saying he'd be down for a drink tonight, but he's headed to a girl's house now. It's 11:15PM, so it's not just me and it's not just her. Our generation is consuming each other's souls in an effort to stave off tomorrow. He didn't even ask me what I was doing. Maybe he was just reporting to me the way you tell your family that you're going for a hike alone and subtly hint that if you're not back by sun-down alarms should be raised. I don't have an emergency contact.

I'm sharing my art with her now. My loft is like a gallery, and while I don't do this art-thing for the panty-drops it precipitates, it is a convenient plus. I need her help hanging an artwork. One might see this as a keen attempt at giving her ownership in this space, but she's fidgety, and I actually need the help. Two arms, two legs, let's get this thing done.

It's crooked. We both have a laugh, but I'm inwardly pissed because I waited all day to get that thing up.

We put on some music and the beatz gods treat us well tonight. The sounds of tonight, so far, are tones of House-Metal fusion. A wood-wick candle tries to sound like a fireplace on my mantle, and a fan spins silently on the ceiling; yet somehow makes a vibration in my head. I've set it's speed to one revolution per second and spend my sleepless nights counting fan blades to make sure the world is working the way I want it to.

This is one of those Open Relationship encounters. I'm emotionally freelance, but she's got a partner at her firm and is doing outside consulting on the behalf of non-possessive love. This is not my first joint exploration of connection. The ventures seem to be universally short explorations of possibility. That could be the nature of the encounter, or it could be me, or it could

111

be that the untold potential for connection in the modern world compels my generation to sift through bodies and personalities in search of the hinted-at-but-never-promised potential energy of a kindred spirit. And it could be that our entitled generation believes that we deserve to happen upon our soulmates as if doing so were as simple as watching movie trailers and deciding upon the night's entertainment. That's what I just did.

Having sex with a stranger is a lot like going to the movies with one. You're both present, and neither of you know exactly what is about to happen, though you both know the plot and you both have expectations. Whether or not you agree on the experience, there's no question that the experience happened, and sometimes you leave with a butter stain on your dress. Not my dress. I don't wear dresses.

I really like movies because, for two hours or so, the rest of the world disappears. If it's a really good movie, I get to replay moments with my imagination and become the protagonist in the story. Also, if you manage to stay in the theater after the show, you can catch a double feature with little to no extra cost.

I feel like tonight is me being a stunt double in my own life. I want the action, the excitement, the thrill of the takedown and the heat of the explosion. I don't want the drama, and I could do without the expectations of the audience after the curtains close. No interviews, no late night talk shows. Just ohhs and ahhs and anonymity. Even so, I'm gearing up for a major performance in my head. I know all the moves already, but timing and execution are key in an action movie. It's not that I'm not being present in the moment, but I'm really looking forward to that hot shower later, and unlike most millennials, I want to earn the trophy I plan on drawing for myself later. The more fantastical it is, the more of the void it will fill up.

The Envelope I NakedThoughts #38

It's 5:49AM in London. This is my thought as I stare through the clock display on my driver's very clean, but shitty, sedan. The time really doesn't matter to me or to my Uber driver, because it's the middle of the fucking night here, and we're very lost.

He's lost; I'm an angry passenger along for the ride. Anger is not a sensation I frequent often. My mood orbits aloof disgruntlement, and the inertia of my mood is so unwavering that it's difficult to push the bar so far as to trigger anger. Today, however, is a day of unmet expectation, and this driver gets to be the book-end on a day of successive failures.

My birthday ended nine minutes ago, right about the moment I reached the end of my midnight walk. I like to pretend that these midnight walks are a novel thing that I do because I'm a creative and I can't sleep at night. I really do them because I'm lonely, and I find being out at night in the cold and wet is an adequate representation of my inner self. I can openly admit to loneliness, and honestly tell you that it has nothing to do with my relationship status. I'm certain now that I've been lonely for the broader part of the past five years, and it has more to do with not having an anchor for my soul than not having someone to put my penis into.

114

Anyway, the thing about the walks is probably true on most occasions, but tonight I had my driver drop me off half a mile from my loft because it took us 40 minutes to drive 13 miles on empty, midnight roads, and I was about to kill him. That's a role reversal from the fears of most ride-share passengers, but I'm pretty sure he felt the tension in the air and is driving away right now convinced all Americans really are murderous.

Let's rewind the clock about 13 hours. I took my first (and a second), tab of LSD today hoping that I would find the boundary at which my ego's territory ends. The place outside of which your 'self' and everything that is not 'you' meet. l have no idea what the fuck I'm talking about, because that stage of the journey never arrived, and I ended up stuck still being me observing myself being high.

The sounds of my acid trip were Yo-Yo Ma waving his magic wand over the strings of a cello to the notes of Bach's Suite No. 2. I laid in bed with my arms wrapped around myself in full corpse mode trying to disappear into the music. And... I saw it. I saw darkness streaked by non-luminescent light that was sound. I knew the lines to be taut strings vibrating a thousand oscillations per instant, such that it looked like solid light crossing the darkness of the envelope of my thoughts which I could not escape. In the dark, I wondered where my feet were, and there, lines of musical light appeared. At first I did not understand, but when my mind looked for the arms that were squeezing me so tightly, the music appeared there, too. I marveled at this new measurement of reality, while knowing that I was still experiencing inside the envelope of the overseer. It was as if my jailer were playing some dirty, ill-conceived ruse on me. Like a lion released by a zookeeper onto safari, expecting it to feel free in its larger enclosure. Instead, I witnessed limits of my range, ironically illuminated by faux freedom, and chose to enjoy the moment, plotting a grander escape all the while.

My disappointment must have wrapped around me like the shadow of an eclipse, because my friend packed up her shit and left once it was apparent that the acid had given-up on expanding my mind. I felt bad that I couldn't have the trip we both wanted me to have, and that she had to leave feeling as though it was her fault. Do drug dealers feel remorse about the misadventures of their clients?

Ever hate yourself so much that you go hang out with friends to melt into their community and not be you for a while? That's how I felt after a few hours of pacing in my loft after Gisse had left. Except, I don't have any friends, so I went to see a musician that I kinda-sorta slept with, who was performing tonight. She was great. The colorfully lit smoke rolling out of the mist machines on stage vibrated with her voice, and the residual hallucinations that rippled across my awareness. A songstress with a weird tick, but an incredible voice. I dug it. I bought her a hot-toddy for her throat after her performance, she wished me a happy birthday, then promptly blew me off. I stood there surrounded by half strangers who laughed at things I said even though I had already forgotten the words. In the vibrating darkness, I wondered what the fuck I was doing there, and decided to call one more disappointment in to round my night out.

Now, I am thinking of my anger as I try to will myself to melt into the couch. Anger is not an emotion. Anger is a sensation. Anger separates you from your feelings. It is an evolutionary tool that protects you from doubt, and fear, and uncertainty, by creating focus and aggression. I have been described as an incredibly calm person. It is a fault of mine because the emotions I keep under surveillance do not have the opportunity to resonate with a person looking to know what is happening in my heart. My calm is a shield I used to supplant anger a long time ago. I don't remember the last time I was angry or hateful directly toward a person. I do remember, however, the angriest I have ever been. It was in a dream. It was such an incredible experience that, after more than a decade, I still remember that dream, and the energy of that wave of emotion I rode. Over time I've learned that the anger that smolders is just a thin but convincing veil to the feelings I am truly harboring. Tonight, that feeling is doubt. Doubt that I can untie the knots that keep me grounded. Or, if I can unbind my own wrists, that I have the wherewithal to reach the bounds of my experience, either aided or unaided, by psychedelic medicine.

117

I can't imagine why anyone would want to be a lion. I made that analogy earlier, but the truth is that a territorial animal rarely extends itself beyond its range. It counts off the paces of its own envelope and accepts the influence of the sphere on its life. I don't want to be a lion.

I'm 33 today, btw.

Note: This NakedThoughts harks on themes in my poetry from days long since passed. But, in the way that there is no such thing as history to the experiential mind, I find myself experiencing the feelings that led to the writing of those old poems again. So, I've included them, unedited and unrevised, in the back of this collection. They were both written in the sophomore year of high school and prove that the unresolved epics of our upbringing resonate with us until remedied. In my case, it feels as though these themes will accompany me forever.

See at the end of this book: "A Devil State of Mind" and "A Stone's Throw Away"

It baffles me to see groups of people traveling and partying together. I don't even have an inner circle, let alone people to travel together with to other hemispheres.

The longest beer-pong match I've ever witnessed continues to unfold, disappointing toss after disappointing toss, in front of me.

I'm the only spectator that seems to care. Maybe that's it; I care too much about ends.

I can't watch TV series either. Same-same, not different.

I'm at a place called Hatch. Whoever laid this egg must love it the same way parents love their disappointing children. They cheer them on from the sidelines and drink to good intentions.

The sounds of today are that of typical bar noise, real and imagined. I'm watching panic roll over the posture of a scruffy surfer in yesterday's clothes as he tries to speak to a group of women. He's grabbing a chair. The woman in the guard position grimaces, and it sounds like a growl in my head. The attractive one is just happy someone finally worked up the courage to speak to her. It looks like he's focusing his attention on the mid-tier catch; the shy one. The beer-pong crew now cheers on a foosball match happening in the shadows, out of sight. Scooters scoot by outside; sound unmuffled.

I'm in Bali, and the walls at a lot of establishments are more suggestions than actual enclosing structures. That's why the staff is whisking away all the cushions as people vacate. It's after midnight, and the sound of Velcro hook and loop being separated as they tear cushions from plywood benches is masochistic; heart-wrenching, yet pleasing. It's the sound I'll imagine when the trio leaves the scruffy guy alone at their table.

The pong group evaporated without my notice. I can hear individual laughter from tables as the bar crowd thins. This place could be really cool if all the colors here didn't make my eyes want to puke muddy rain-bows. This place is like a seventies fitness show collided with a tree house and their disappointed parents gave everyone alcohol afterward, then left them to sort out the chaos unsupervised.

My observation tonight is tainted by a bitters-encrust-ed loneliness derived from the insight that I don't actu-ally want to get to know anyone here, but I wish that I had company. Relationships are a lot like a never-end-ing beer-pong match; we all keep missing the cup and at some point, we become too invested in the game to walk away. The game stops mattering, and you're either trying to prove something to yourself, or sticking around to ensure the other players are just as aimless as you are.

A last table of friends pours a round of drinks from a frothy pitcher, and I wish they knew me well enough to let me be over here by myself choosing my ends.

Fate | NakedThoughts #40

I figure Fate is something like Google maps. There are waypoints on your agenda and Fate relentlessly reroutes you to them no matter how fucked up your life choices are. At the end of life, Fate tallies up the cost of getting you to where you needed to be, and hands you a receipt. You know the toll already, because you can feel it.

I'm in the airport feeling the weight of judging eyes. I question the mechanics of collective consciousness. In a book I'm writing, reality is the agreed upon consensus of the mind at large. Let's take that to be true (because who TF knows what's right in this realm). So couldn't the sum of my life also be tallied by the collection of consciousnesses that witness it?

If all the people in this terminal shared their thoughts about me, would the average of their musings be truth? Would a curve be applied to their opinions based upon how familiar with me they are? What is the nominal factor of intuition? Who or what would measure the cumulative report? God?

God is a funny word. What other word with so vague a definition is fought over so virulently? Not even menstruation has spilled as much blood, (probably not true).

My plane is about to take off. My Bose headphones' noise-canceling can't compute the roar of this 777's General Electric GE90 Turbo Fan engines and the result is a crackling in my earphones that I've never heard before. Up until now, the sounds of today have been the all-but-ignored safety prompts from the flight crew. I actually hung a towel over the headset tv that was playing the safety video so that I didn't have to watch. Instead, I've been eavesdropping on the couple behind me as they negotiate the rationing of spare battery power. They're young and seem cool. My row has two seats on this side of the aisle and the old lady next to me seems so old that she will probably die several times on this flight, and no one will know. The perma-scowl on her face already tells me that we will not be speaking. This is great news because old ladies invariably end up offering me their daughters and grand-daughters, and I have to smile, act bashful, and make non-committal noises until they give up.

On the other side of fate is causality. Every step in the journey is the product of an equation comprised of an incomprehensibly tangled web of consequences. To believe in causality is to believe, in the most practical and analytical manner, that axiom, "everything happens for a reason". Nothing can, or will, happen any differently because of the algebra of life. The sum of the past equals the present and the future is a calculation waiting to be computed. This school of thought suggests that you are in control and accountable for your future, but you're really not. Your past wields your present like a pole-arm with a carrot on the end.

I was never much for my vegetables, to be honest. They interest me as a unit of measure, though. I can always tell how much someone cares about me by how steadfast they are about me eating healthy. My mother doesn't even fuss about it anymore. Out of sight, out of mind.

I've upgraded my seat on this flight to Premium. I'm on some "manifesting your future by pretending it's already here," shit. It's like fake-it-til-you-make-it but with higher stakes. The extra spend has granted me legroom, a quiet isle companion, and a window that displays my life passing me by in an oval metaphor. In metaphoric style, I pull the window shade down. I don't have any control over where life takes me for the next two hours, I'm in between waypoints.

The receipt for my seat upgrade states, "retain for entire journey" and I wonder if I'm back on the right path in life or if the GPS is still rerouting. We're all grievously (grudgingly), weighed down with life's useless receipts.

Interlude:

The void is an interesting place, and I observe it often. When you stare into the abyss, it reveals its nature and that is what I think people fear when they say, "the abyss stares back". My observations: the void is inside me, and therefore has boundaries. It is black, but I acknowledge it, and therefore it must also have light. It is bottomless, but it consumes life to feel sated; it cannot be bottomless. In fact, I'm not sure the void exists inside of me at all. If it did, that which would fill it would first have to go through the filter of me, and my ego is not acknowledging anything at the moment. It's like a singularity that wraps itself around its owner like the cloak of a maleficent antagonist in a medieval movie. It shields me from a world desperately attempting to express value toward me. The blackhole only fails when the bearer is strong enough to throw the cloak over his shoulder and bear the pressure of a world strewn with fountains of abundance.

Well, I don't want any of that shit right now. My pool is too shallow for fountains of bullshit, and this trickle of hot bodily contact is all that I need to keep my heart hydrated and beating toward its own ends. I part the cloak to let in what little about the world I can understand, then zip it up tight again. This is my current reality.

I heard a smart person say that the fourth dimension could be defined by mathematics. If that is true, then love must not reside there. Love must exist in the fifth dimension. We know it exists, but it's undefinable and intangible. Merely observing it would destroy it.

I'm thinking about love just now because I made this pork chop and it was totally rad. I'd give it an 8 out of 10 for incredible flavor and texture.

I'm observing the carnage in my kitchen, and I'm remembering the taste: I know I could do it better. Make it more... more. Which has ever been my experience with love.

Now that the cooking has ceased, and I've devoured all that I care to, the only sound present is that of my procrastination. It sounds like the echo of me doing work in the future. It's annoying. There is a ticking sound that puzzles me because I don't own a clock and the ice in my empty whiskey-coke cracks as it too recognizes the carnage of fully consumed love, and releases its hold on itself with a sigh.

In four dimensional space you can see the inside of a thing. Schrödinger's Cat would never have been a mystery, and neither would a love story; a four dimensional consciousness would witness the inner and surface layers of the heart simultaneously. Imagine knowing what you wanted to eat at the same time you asked after it. Impossible. So love can't be the fourth dimension.

Still. I knew this pork chop was going to be the one before I dropped it in my oil-filled pan. That transcended time and space up until the moment I observed it. Then it was here. Now it is gone.

PS. I wrote this drunk and I'm not going to edit it.

Extra | NakedThoughts #42

I can't decide what this one particular construction worker's purpose is. She's become a resident at this crossing these past few weeks. She's not a sign holder; she just stands in the intersection like one of the stanchions. When I'm driving straight through the intersection, she waves me through. When I'm turning, she signals me to turn. Is she directing me, or do the turn signals on my Jeep instruct her how to wave her arms? This is all she does. Like a soccer mom coaching from the sideline, she brings no value to the task at hand. Even still, all the players on the field accept her presence as inevitable.

The minivan's license plate in front of me reads "Cee Ya", and now I am forced to have two ideas battle for dominance in my head. One idea constantly repeats "Wouldn't want to be ya", and I hate the car for allowing that juvenile facet of my psyche something to latch on to. The other thought process is trying to make an argument about the driver needing to have met me before that statement attains any validity. The second thought is pointedly ignoring the juvenile's chanting in my head while pitying me for having to suffer it. This is my house of cards, after all.

I'm driving to get a pedicure. I get one every time I make a big sale in my art business. My toenails seem to grow at the speed of which my bank accounts diminish. Odd that. Perhaps, my ability to recognize my need for self-care is commensurate with my feelings of security and legitimacy as an independent, successful artist and entrepreneur. Sheesh, I need a massage. The chair will have those rolly-things and I will vigorously attack the backrest with my weight.

Ever consider the magnitude of the fact that somebody built all the things around you? Someone made these uniquely purposed massage chairs with water buckets at the feet. Someone also blew the glass of the odd-shaped tincture flask next to the chair. It is obviously mislabeled "Charcoal" since the contents are clear and somehow a plumeria is growing within it. Someone even made... me. Well, two someones. Everything is made, and much of it is a bit... extra.

I think people should stop making things. By 'things' I mean people. There, I said it. If the world has too much of anything it is people. We've outgrown our environ-ment, and the extra people are ruining it. This is really the only ecological discussion that matters. Predictably, this is the one that no one will address. Humans. How can we reduce the number of carbon-emitting vehicles? Stop making people to drive them. How do we reduce the unprecedented amount of deforestation committed to produce soy beans (and such)? Stop making people that consume soy (and such). Want to double the odds of finding a certain someone in the fornication farce we call dating? Increase your odds by halving the sup-ply; by making less people.

129

I'm sitting at Cyprus Coffee. My toes feel extra roomy in my shoes. The sounds of today are drowned out by the "Creative Flow" blasting in my headphones. It's an audio amalgamation of a loud stream that I like to imagine is rain-fed, since it is pouring in real life. A bored orchestra accompanies the stream, and an intense heartbeat makes everything seem imminent. The music is also my excuse to not acknowledge the people around me in the name of concentration. A relatively attractive woman with a cat-inspired backpack just sat directly in the vector of my thinking face, and now out of politeness, I should stare blankly elsewhere... I've resolved not to do so while writing that last sentence. I may not own the tunnel of space my vision is consuming but neither does she. Instead, I'll imagine her not existing at all. Would this coffee shop be half empty if we stopped making extra people? I doubt it. There would simply be fewer coffee shops. More green things. Fewer minivans, more room to enjoy the road. Less doom and less gloom. More zen.

This argument for the preservation of our future will never happen on the political stage. If it were a tincture, it'd be too hard to swallow. Instead, we are passively manufacturing the next mass extinction event which, in itself, is a solution for the preservation of our future insofar as it's not too extra. Taking a look around this room and its four-person, stained plank tables, bench-style seating arrangements, and steel, non-cushioned chairs, I see that one in three people are of the older generations. The boomers and the doom bringers. If the aging generations of the world, the Gen O's and W's, were able to pile into a minivan, the collective's license plate would say "Cee Ya".

Suburbia | NakedThoughts #43

I'm visiting hell on earth today. Suburbia.

Okay, maybe it's not one of Dante's 9 circles. If Hell were a solar system, then suburbia would be the Kuiper Belt. A distant region of space, filled with comets that worlds occasionally crash through, destroying life as we know it. When I find my life passing through Hell's Kuiper Belt, I hold my breath, cast prayers out like they're a force field of some kind, and screw my eyes almost shut. I can't not look but I also can't bear to watch. I'm afraid of this place and what it represents. It's pervasiveness. Its seeming inevitability.

This suburb of Seattle is a maze of single-story dwellings with unused yards watched over by picture-windows jutting from living room walls like bulbous eyes. All the curtains are drawn, as if the occupants don't actually want to look outside, they just want the opportunity to do so. They want the privilege not to do so. The featureless streets are spotted with the occasional stunted tree, so uninspired that it gave up on growing tall once it realized there was nothing to see over the rooftops. The homes here seem so laced with depression that the way the cars slump against their suspension on the slightly inclined driveways uniformly pitched from the curbsides appear to me as resigned dogs, locked out of their dog houses, that are dreaming of being elsewhere. The garages where they would be warm and happy are instead repurposed as caches of 'almost's' and 'forgotten's'. They're filled with yesterday's over-appropriated, abused goods, kept forever because the past always seems a bit brighter than the future.

I grew up in a suburb similar to this, and I believe that this is the birthplace of my delusions of grandeur. Too young to imagine being somewhere else, as a kid I imagined being someone else. I wanted to be a hero. I imagined flying fighter jets, shooting beams of energy from my hands... beating up the bully at school. I might have been the bully at school, but... no. The person I was meanest to was myself.

Growing older, I equated heroism with manhood, and my imaginings became more synced with reality. I still want to fly and shoot beams of energy from my hands, but I also want to tackle the gunman, wrestle a bear, save a damsel... run a successful business. The more impossible or unlikely these imaginings become, the more at odds I am with my masculinity. I wonder constantly if I have earned it.

One of the reasons I don't believe in "the universe", is that I have invited so much violence into my life and have seen none of it. I remember midnight walks in Afghanistan, alone and cloaked in darkness, inviting the nefarious elements of Jalalabad over the dirt embankments to try my worthiness. The thing that strikes me most as I recall those twenty-minute hikes along the flight line, was how recklessly I wanted the fight. I never got it. My time there passed little to write home about.

I often question my honesty during the discourse I have with myself. I am obviously spending too much time in my own head.

I still have midnight walks. This evening is was oddly quiet. The omnipresent roar of the nearby highway notwithstanding, I heard nothing but my feet on wet pavement, and the occasional scurrying of rabbits too fear-brained to realize that they were in the least danger while they remained motionless. Or, perhaps, the rabbits are eager to prove their agility by darting away from me. While I'm always on the lookout for a bear or a pair of over-zealous coyotes on my urban-orbiting mountainside, tonight I wrestled with the notion that the fight I've really been trying to win is the idea that I'm not man-enough to be me. That is, the person I claim to be.

I don't even know what that fucking means. It might be that I wrestle with the idea of mediocrity, and whether or not being a regular dude is also being a man. I wonder if imagining the fight is the equivalent of filling my garage with the almost-heroic versions of myself. The Kuiper Belt of Hell exists in my mind and suburbia reminds me that it's there. I'm thirty-three and I am still reimagining my superhero self. My current iteration is highly nihilistic. I have the power to annihilate anything. To completely remove a thing from existence. I would use those powers to annihilate landfills and garbage dumps. Maybe the great plastic patch in the Pacific. Occasionally I'd poof an asshole or two, but like all warriors, the battle without is mirrored within. What I should be destroying is my garage.

Standing in the shower beneath the diminishing heat, willing it to stay warm, is the futility of life compressed into a bathroom experience.

Naked, as these things go, I'm standing beneath steam-less water turning the temperature knob toward the red crescendo to no avail. I know this effort will produce no increased heat. Instead, I'm turning the knob of denial and trying to persuade my body to enjoy the lesser warmth as the mercury in this think tank, which is what I call my shower when I'm talking to myself, travels toward lukewarm. As the temperature fades, reality comes crashing in as though the volume of steam filling the bathroom had kept it at bay.

In this moment, my life-long pursuit of riches is solely focused on acquiring longer, luxurious showers. It's more of a visualization than a pursuit. I'm 33 and have spent 15 years visualizing wealth. If I spent that same volume of time actually pursuing greater income, I might have some measure of it.

Is time a volume? If it is, is it shrinking or expanding? I mean, the universe is expanding with time. The science, if you subscribe to such a thing, has proven that. The universe is propelled forth in all directions on the heat waves of the Big Bang. But, the universe and the time that accompanies it, is infinite. I am not infinite; there's no dark matter expanding my experience (except for, maybe, rum). So, if time is a volume, is my time shrinking around me? Perhaps the existential fear I experience is actually conceptual claustrophobia.

Or! If it is a volume that is expanding, how would I keep the space filled? Instead of a shrinking bubble of existence in which I wink out of being, I expand into the void that I cannot fill, and become insignificant, then wink out of existence. The fear then would be agoraphobia. The result the same.

The sounds of shower thoughts are that of faux rain, if rain were to come out of a pipe screaming at you. The droplets are small, so the voices are small and metallic. Perhaps they scream at suddenly enter a space larger than imagination, after being shredded from their mates. Or, are they shredded from one contiguous identity into many? I don't know, but after an interminable time it all crashes on to the stone floor at my feet, and that's the rain-part of the sounds of my shower.

Maybe babies arrive screaming into the world for the same reason. The volume of their world suddenly expands from vagina-sized cavity to... the world. Like, its first stop on the long tracks of life is Grand Central Station, and it'd loud and cacophonous and immense. Does its time start shrinking from then?

137

Visualize a subway tunnel leading away from Grand Central Station. The sounds of Grand Central are the thousandth and ten-thousandth echoes of passing trains commingling into a chorus so constant and cacophonous that you forget it is there. The air is filled with people having conversations with people, and people having conversations with themselves, aloud. Rolling luggage sounds like the distant cousin of the subway trains, many times removed, and for some reason, when people walk past with food, you can hear how good it tastes. Time begins in the massive central terminal with its vaulted, decorated ceiling, and ticket counters. You can ask for directions at the kiosk in the center of the space, if you don't know where to go. The elders there are always bored with traveler naïveté, yet happy to tell you where to go. You peer down the particular subway tunnel that is your life, and perspective forces all the lines to converge to a point. Some tunnels are lit and certain. Others are dark. Those lines converging aren't a phenomenon of perspective and distance, though. That convergence is the volume of time you have left shrinking away. The further down the tunnel you travel, the more you have to squeeze the things that fill your experience into the diminishing volume your life is afforded.

Let the tunnel be elastic, like a condom (or something), and let the pursuits in our lives be expansive, like heat. I'm not trying to make the tunnel longer, just big enough to enjoy till the end, (that's what she said). The heats in our lives are sex, money, and drugs.

Maybe love and connection, and really, really good food, too. There is something about the smashing together of lives and bodies that makes heat. It is the hardest heat to hold onto, though. It is always pulling itself away; ebbing and flowing on its own accord. Much energy is used in trying to contain it. Fill the space with wealth, because wealth can attract the things that make heat, and wealth can buttress the tunnel in the heat's absence. But... it's still cold.

Some optimal combination of human friction and tech seems required to make this journey comfortable to the end. I don't have much of either to keep my volume of time expanded. I'm rubbing two pennies together for heat, and hoping that maybe they'll multiply. The effort proves fruitless, of course. I know I'm only in my thirties, but I can feel the walls closing in. They say love is the answer, but love doesn't pay the electric bill, and I've never seen a human produce enough warmth to push the chill out of my bathroom after a shower. It's all futile, like I said. So I'll keep turning the knob and hoping for the best.

Whiskey and Tea | NakedThoughts #45

Today's waitress is committed to getting me drunk. I requested hot water and she asked me a second time if I'd like a double. Granted, the hot water is to refresh my whiskey-tea, but it's 10:15AM. Doubles are for afternoons.

I'm in the airport, plagiarizing ideas. I guess this is called "looking for inspiration" but I'm no fan of semantics.

I feel spread thin lately. Not in the 'there's not enough of me to go around' way. I feel like a mostly transparent gas, occupying a useless container. I have always felt that I am not the person people think I am. I feel like I am not the person I thought I was. You know the way Double Stuff Oreos cost $4.99, just like they did years ago, but there're less Oreos in the racks now? I feel like I've been pick-pocketed, but the thief is the lies I tell myself, and what was stolen was my substance. I'm somehow less substantial than expected, but the toll is the same.

How do I fix that, though? I need to make more 'me' on the inside, and use it to fill this space that I occupy. This meat sack of failing expectations. Ingredients; I need something sticky that will plug the holes in the sac, something hot like a fireplace people warm themselves by, and something heavy that will keep my unsubstantiated persona from flailing in the impassive winds. The Social Winds and the Crosswinds of Expectation. The Down Drafts of all the wasted potential that people see in me, and the violent Updrafts of Hope.

What do you make this stuff with? Hot alcohol and condensed dreams? Vitamin B? Taurine? This morning, as the sun scoots across the sky, it is whiskey.

The sounds of this restaurant are those of a breakfast bar becoming a lunchtime bar. It is suddenly cacophonous, suddenly crowded, suddenly claustrophobic. The waitress is Vietnamese. She calls everybody 'Honey' and 'Baby' with long annunciations on the soft vowels. She sounds exactly like the prostitute from Full Metal Jacket, and maybe a little like the way Bilquis from American Gods sounded in my head when she ate a worshiper with her vagina. Neil Gaiman made that meal seem much more gratifying than my visionless chicken-biscuit-grits breakfast. Whiskey Tea being the only saving grace.

I think I just figured out what my problem is. Separated by a comfortable yet eaves-droppable distance are two old guys sharing animated stories over a hot coffee and what appears to be a lemonade.

They are gossiping. One guy is the listener; white haired and leaning forward on his elbows intently. He's well dressed in standard PNW attire; a vest and hiking

141

boots. The other is dark haired under a ball cap, and wearing a hoodie and shorts. The second is doing all the talking, while the first nods appropriately and occasionally leans back in his seat to guffaw with equal energy as his counterpart's story ebbs and flows.

The old guy and the waitress are quite similar in their determination to make their people feel attended to. They are the sticky stuff in the ingredients I need. Listening to her greet people gives me a face splitting grin. The guy in the hat makes me wish I had a white haired, vest wearing, steamy cup holding, appropriately guffawing guy to remind me that I am substantial, too.

"Here you go, Babeee" she says as she places a mug of hot water on a plate in front of me. There's another shot of whiskey next to it.

Postlude

I'm sitting at a bar, editing the very book that this might be included in. My headphones are in and blasting Hans Zimmer so that the rest of the world might not exist. Still, I can hear.

The guy next to me is telling his mom about his friend in LA. I'd like it if he'd not speak over my music. The kid on my left is bawling his eyes out. I hated him five minutes ago when he wouldn't stop knocking my chair, and now I'd like him to die. His dad is parenting, and between tracks, I learn that the kid might, or might not have, had a blast pulling all the paper towels out of the dispenser in the bathroom.

Did I mention this is a breakfast bar?

It's nearly lunch time, and apparently, I'm not the only person to tell the clock to "suck it" this morning. My food is slow in coming, the kid on my left ain't done crying, the guy next to me is apparently NOT talking to his mom (I'll let you draw conclusions there), and my stomach is preparing for an afternoon of wheat intolerance. It's like Bulimia, but instead of forcing you to seek help, everyone shuns you; even the dog.

I hope there's some tissue left in the bathroom.

A Note from the Author

It seems kind of asinine to write that this is a "note from the author", the entire book has been notes from me, but that is how convention would have it. I wanted to tell you about some other things I'm up to at the moment, and where you can find me on the Internet so that, if you wanted to, you could give me a virtual high five.

At the time of this writing, I have about five different story lines that I am writing, including Naked-Thoughts, because NakedThoughts is a never ending project. I have three separate epic fantasy story lines being developed by my overactive imagination. How overactive is my imagining? I literally created an entire world in my head two weeks ago while strolling along on my one mile midnight walk. In addition to those, I am working on a compilation of short stories that are based on my dreams. I am calling this book "Dream Daggers & Imaginary Friends." It will likely be my next book release. For your reading pleasure, I've included one of my favorite dreams following this note. I hope you can enjoy my craziness as much as I sometimes do.

Connect With Me

Friend me on Facebook: "Jason Matias"
My writing account on instagram: @thewhiskeyruns
Follow my photography: www.jasonmatias.com &
@realjasonmatias
Subscribe to my mailing list: www.jasonmatias.com/
nakedthoughts

THANK YOU SO MUCH FOR READING MY
THOUGHTS!
Please leave a review for this book
wherever you bought this copy.

Dream Daggers & Imaginary Friends
Flying Whales | 31 May 2016

For as long as I can remember, the sky was alive with schools of flying fish and mantas that glided on the wind. You could always look up and see a familiar shape exploring what seemed to be a limitless kingdom that began where I stood, and extended far into the heavens. The sky was as full of handsome, graceful, and nimble fish, as it was spotted with terrifying predators and living storms with lightning that attacked, and rolling clouds that consumed.

At times the sky seemed impossibly full of life. Those were the times you felt the smallest. Other times the sky could be so empty; a pale blue infinity. During those times, you felt the most insignificant; as if the void above were a measuring tool so vast that you could not see the first mark, let alone strive for it. There was more than flying fish in the sky; there were birds, too. Great birds as large as a small truck. Wings so powerful that they could blow a man over. As a flock, they could take down enormous flying fish and tear them apart before they hit the ground.

Beautiful and majestic though it was, nature was indifferent to how fragile a man really was. The ranch I lived on in this dream was merely an access to a home built underground for protection. This was not a world conquered by man. At best, our preservation went unnoticed by nature and its beautiful demons. At worst, nature and the heavens conspired to keep us tiny, and our feet on the ground.

I watched Mark through the doorway; a middle-aged man in rough jeans and a thick work shirt, as he sat motionless, in quiet awe. His posture was one of fear, slightly overpowered by amazement. He leaned forward, hands on his knees, ready to bolt at the first hint of danger, but he couldn't tear his eyes from nature's raw display above. I couldn't see what was happening, but I heard it, and I could see the flashes of blue-white light. A lightning storm had collided with a flock of birds pursuing a massive school of fish. The enormous sounds; like Earth sighing through lungs like a giant earthen wineskin with a thousand musical holes, like a thousand wheezing trumpets... those were flying whales. Each one unique in both variety and temperament. They chased the storms and ate the carcasses and carrion that rained from them. My favorite whale had three jaws, and was so old that the earth seemed to grow from its carapace. It was more like a flying mountain than a living animal. I'd seen him twice. This was not the first time I'd been in this dream.

A bird crashed with a sickening crunch in the field outside the house. Its body was already mauled before it crumpled and shattered on the ground, probably caught in the maw of the storm. The field outside was

147

cleared for one hundred meters in every direction, so that anyone on watch could have enough time to see a predator coming out of the wilderness; both on the ground, and over the horizon. I found myself standing on the porch next to Mark. The sky was a rolling mass of boiling clouds, and blue-green lightning. Between the deafening thunder, the roaring winds, and the trumpeting of flying whales, we could hear the anguish and wailing of a thousand, thousand animals colliding in desperation. The cacophony was the indifference of nature. The sound made my bones vibrate, and controlled the pace of my heart. A column of roiling clouds lit from within by a dim, blue-tinted light reached down from its mass, and intercepted an enormous school of frenzied, racing fish, erasing a massive chunk of their numbers as if sweeping dust from a table. A whale as long as a city block flew next to the column, dwarfed like an average bird against the sky.

Above our cleared patch of land, another whale punched out of lightless clouds; the vapor sticking to its skin like oil. Dozens of flying fish and mantas crashed to the ground ahead of it, and a flock emerged; daggers in the night, tearing them apart as they fell. The Eagles crashed into the whale like broad-head arrows, and its wail nearly vibrated my bones to dust.

I found myself in the house, searching for a rifle. Everything in the house jumped as the whale slammed into the earth outside. I ran down the corridor to the porch. Outside, I could see the eagles shredding the

148

whale. Ten steps. Everything was in slow motion. I charged my scoped rifle; the small caliber round found its home in the chamber. Seven steps. So many wings and feathers in motion I could barely see the whale. Five steps. I saw a glimpse of bone. Two steps. I could see straight through the frenzy. The barrel rose as I burst through the open door, and I sighted the cross-hairs on a bare carcass. The birds were gone. The bones were picked so clean that they were chipped and crumbling in places. I lowered the gun in disbelief, and frustration. Mark stared at me with an absent expression. "You scared them away." he said.

Then I woke up.

A Devil's State of Mind

All it is
Is a compounding hate.
One which, like dough
Rises, expands, and fills
With a disgust that
Like fear, which grows into aggression
Festers into a devil state of mind
That as a roach which incessantly taps your window in
the middle of the night
Bangs at the gates of his mind with the rooted end of a
rotted trunk
Moaning and wailing as a ghoul might
Crying to be free to unleash and destroy
Like an enraged panther amongst sleeping hunters.
    Like a crazed rhino with beet red eyes screaming at
the sun
For boiling its skin
It sets fire to its world behind the gates
Only to writhe in pain and rise with rancor in redden-
ing embers
To heave its smoldering body
Against the gates one more time.
    Like a feral bat that can no longer bear the harrow-
ing
Torment of its own discord
It tightens its larynx and bellows in anguish
To plunge its taut body
Against the gates one more time.

Like a ram embittered by the frailty of its spiral
horns
Irked by the crippling pain ripping through its spine
It rises in primordial fury
To charge its grisly frame
Against the gates one more time.
   Like a man on his knees in despair
Burrowing deep, burying it
Driven to create the devil
Guilted to stand before its tempest
   Like a man in a dire condition
Heels entrenched, body wrought in searing pain
Face scorched, cracked, and tear'd dry in agony.
The only buttress to the gates of his own deranged hate
And only one forlorn thought on his withered, quiver-
ing lips:
Why brace the gates with this broken body
One last time.

~ Jason Matias

151

A Stone's Throw Away

When the glowing foothill crests the plain at
A thousand yards view
The fluids of a body spur
As if a stone has plunged into a ready but
Stagnant pool of hopes and dreams
And at the trough a dormant love lies
Ardent, and poised to escalate to the crest

And when the foothill becomes
A flush mound and dense shimmering rays
Pierce a bare chest
Riveting aspirations collapse inwards about
A vacancy left by a stone
Colliding and bounding to an apex
Of a sparkling spiral spire
On top of which there is only room for one

And when that globe rises, shedding vibrant glimmer-
ing zeal
Illuminating an obsidian crater in which the pool
seems a puddle
Hope is left appalled and utterly enlightened that
When the ripples fade
And the lights go out
Salvation is still a stone's throw away.

~Jason Matias